Nine Witnesses
For The Colonel

Nine Witnesses
For The Colonel

King Charles' most faithful servant

Elaine T. Joyce

BREWIN BOOKS

BREWIN BOOKS
56 Alcester Road,
Studley,
Warwickshire,
B80 7LG
www.brewinbooks.com

Published by Brewin Books 2019

© Elaine T. Joyce, 2019

A CIP catalogue record for this book is available
from the British Library.

ISBN: 978-1-85858-586-4

Printed and bound in Great Britain
by 4edge Ltd.

Contents

Colonel William Careless

"A subject faithful to the King"

Preface

I have been researching this book for well over forty years. As my family were English Catholics, I often wondered if they had been so through penal times. When my Aunt Nina died and we cleared out her house we found Catholic prayer books which had belonged to my great grandmother Elizabeth Carless. From the census I found that her father was Joseph Careless, son of John Careless. I thought it was amusing that the 'e' had been dropped so that it sounded better. It was difficult to trace further back but when I visited Boscobel and heard the story of Colonel Careless I wondered if we might be descended from him. Disappointingly, I still have not proved any connection but his life story fascinated me. I have uncovered some facts not generally known before, such as where his wife was buried and how his son the priest died, and I hope other readers will find his heroic life as interesting as I do.

Lichfield Record Office, where I spent many pleasant hours researching has now sadly closed. The staff were always extremely helpful to me, as also is the case at Stafford Record Office and the fascinating William Salt Library.

I also wish to thank Fr. John Sharp and Naomi Johnson at the Birmingham Archdiocesan Archives, the National Trust and the Victoria and Albert Museum. Special thanks go to Malcolm Atkin, the author of The Battle of Worcester 1651, who kindly gave me permission to reproduce his map showing the movements of the two armies towards Worcester.

I am very grateful to Doctor Judith Champ at St. Mary's College Oscott for her explanation to me of how Jesuits are trained and also to Mary Allen at the Jesuit archives who supplied me with obscure information about Father William Carlos alias Dorrington. Heartfelt thanks also to my husband and my sister for reading my book and making helpful suggestions, to my son for his patient help with computer difficulties, my daughter for her encouraging comments and all my family and friends who have patiently listened to my obsession!

This is not an unbiased view of history. It is written from the point of view of real people who lived in the seventeenth century during civil war and religious persecution. They were passionately committed to their politics, beliefs and loyalties and were ready to lay down their lives for a cause. Commonplace individuals became heroes; this story is about one ordinary man, who might have led an unknown humdrum life on his farm, but instead became the hero of the nation.

Prologue

Boscobel c.1820

All light was draining from the wintry December sky as twilight drew on; the drizzle of rain began to fall gloomily, with a gentle weariness. Ellen had been working in the garden laying white pebbles in a pattern of words to commemorate King Charles II, but was driven indoors by the damp and the cold. Tired, she sat in a comfortable chair by the fireside in the parlour and as the darkness deepened her thoughts wandered drowsily over the history of this old house. Her step-father Walter Evans had bought Boscobel and spent much time and money restoring it to how he thought it had appeared in Stuart times and decorated it with scenes of Charles' escape after the Battle of Worcester. Two hundred years ago, in this very room as she believed, the young dark haired, dark complexioned monarch had sat by this hearth, poking the embers into flames. She seemed to see him in her mind's eye, tossing the collops of mutton into a pan; she could almost hear him laughing as the meat sizzled in the butter and he prattled on, joking with the stocky, older soldier at his side.

"What was his companion like?" the young woman wondered. His name was well-known, Colonel Careless, but where did he come from? What family did he have and what happened to him after this remarkable encounter with the King of England?

"If only I could go back into the past and meet him, talk to him and find out what character he had," she murmured as her thoughts began to slip away from her with the onset of sleep. "What part did he play in the Civil War, and how did his adventure in the Oak Tree at Boscobel affect the rest of his life?" As the darkness increased, between being awake and sleeping, it seemed to her that the shadows in the corners and recesses of the ancient room were gathering and forming into figures, which became more definite by the minute. Nine people were approaching her, dressed in old-fashioned clothes of many generations ago. Two were in simple countrymen's apparel, one a better class yeoman, the other seeming to be a labourer. Two were in Royalist officers' uniform, with all the assured bearing of gentlemen. A sweet-faced, patient looking woman, stepped forward timidly towards Ellen with anxious eyes, as though she had waited a lifetime for some tidings. Standing next to her were two priests, one middle-aged yet frail, the other old yet sprightly, settled in experience and wisdom.

Dominating them all with his stature and his presence was the monarch, Charles himself, with a half-smile upon his heavy mouth, as though he was about to make a jest or utter one of his witty sayings. The last person that Ellen noticed was a youngish man, seeming to be of middle-class or trade, who appeared moderately prosperous, judging by his good quality clothes.

The yeoman began to speak, in a voice with a Staffordshire county accent which she found hard to follow at first, for he was talking in a style and pronunciation of two hundred years ago. As her ear became accustomed to his speech, she became aware he was telling her about Colonel Careless.

"Because you have been thinking so much about the events that happened in and around this house and because your interest in William Careless is so great, we have come to tell you about his life. Each of us knew him well; he affected each one of us, with his courage, his loyalty and his complete reliability. The warmth of his character and the generosity of his heroic nature added quality not only to our lives, but to the whole spirit of English history. Listen and we will tell you, the story of a man of outstanding bravery—my brother William Careless."

CHAPTER 1

Testimony of John Careless, tenant of Broom Hall

Carelesse, Carless, Carles, Carlos and Carlis, are all various forms of my family name, meaning free from care, and perhaps we were in generations far distant; but in these later, troubled times we are, on the contrary, full of cares and troubles. A respectable, hard-working yeoman farming family, for as far back as memories go we have tended the farm at Broom Hall, deep in the heart of Staffordshire, near the small town of Brewood. It is a good sizeable farm with meadows for grazing sheep, large fields for crops, as well as a comfortable house; barns to store the hay we harvest, outbuildings to shelter our animals and a fruit orchard, which has fair blossoms in spring turning to sweet apples in autumn.

Different parts of the estate were owned by two old, well respected families of gentry status, the Lanes and the Giffards. Our present landlords are both Royalist gentlemen; Colonel John Lane, who lives at Bentley Hall with his spirited daughter Jane and Mr Peter Giffard, who lives at a fine, large house, Chillington Hall, a few miles away from here, the other side of Brewood. One of my ancestors, Thomas Careless was a tenant of Sir John Giffard, back in 1556, during the time of Mary Tudor. My dear parents, John

Careless and my mother Eleanor, were granted the lease of Broom Hall in 1599, from John Lane. John Giffard let them have the lease to the other parts of the farm in 1611, when the old King James was ruling England. My parents had three sons, Edward, myself John and my restless brother William.

The situation became difficult for my ancestors during the reign of the Protestant Queen Elizabeth, because they were devoutly Catholic and as persecutions raged and Recusants were fined heavily, they at times paid dearly for the Faith they treasured, but at other times they kept quiet and secret. My father, who was most obstinate in his views, was named as Recusant in 1600, that is to say he was a Roman Catholic person who would not attend the services of the established Church of England, as was required by the laws of that harsh Queen.

The Old Faith was kept alive in Staffordshire by some of the wealthy, Catholic gentry; the Giffards of Chillington, the family who owned part of our Broom Hall estate, kept a chapel where Mass continued to be said, and it was the same at Moseley Hall with the Whitgreave family. Peter Giffard paid a huge amount, £140 a year, for his recusancy and was accused in 1639 that he "for many years past aided and relieved and received into his house Roman papistical priests, where living 120 miles from town he had been a partaker of Mass."

Priests would be sheltered at these houses, often living disguised as a tutor. We less wealthy families, who still loved the Catholic church, were glad to be able to attend Mass, albeit secretly and fearfully, stealing often by night into dark and dusty garrets, receiving the Eucharist in pewter vessels that would pass for everyday household cups and platters, rather than the gold or silver chalices that the Holy Sacrament deserved. Things continued in this way during the time of Scottish King James and his son Charles I. We were brought low in our fortunes, through fines and penalties, however hard we worked the land.

There were many Catholics in Staffordshire, more I believe than in many other counties. In our neighbouring small town of Brewood, eighty-six names were counted when the authorities conducted a survey of Papists at Epiphany and Easter, in 1641. Over a thousand were counted in the County of Staffordshire, and one hostile Puritan at Willenhall, Richard Lee, wrote of Wolverhampton, that "I never knew any part of this kingdom where Rome's snakie brood roosted and rested themselves more warmer and safer and with greater countenance than in this country."

Most of our Protestant neighbours tolerated us quite well, especially when we dutifully attended the Anglican church in Brewood, keeping it quiet that we also crept stealthily to the secret Masses at Chillington Hall or Moseley Hall. At times of unrest and trouble however, such as when in my early childhood Fawkes and his conspirators tried to blow up the Old Stuart King James and his Parliament, or when in 1641 there were many malicious rumours rife of the atrocities the Catholic rebels were inflicting on the Protestants of Ireland, there would be murmuring and threats and suspicious looks from the people in the town of Brewood. Then indeed we were fearful that measures would be taken against us, that we would face higher fines or worse imprisonment, and so we had to be careful. Several of the wealthier Catholic gentry would build a secret hiding place into their house, so that if the authorities came searching, hoping to find a visiting priest, he could be hidden safely away, often under floorboards or behind privies. Although these priests' holes were cramped and uncomfortable, it was better than being hauled into prison or execution. The Catholics of the area knew these places and were practised in being discreet, resourceful and trustworthy.

As troubles between the first King Charles and his Parliament grew stronger, like dark clouds threatening a great storm over our land, we Catholics became fearful of how it would be if the Puritans had all the power of government. We had more hopes of tolerance from the King, whose French wife, Henrietta Maria, was a Catholic and who was allowed to have her own chapel, and priests to say Mass for her.

My brother William married a lady named Dorothy Fox from up Stafford way, and they had two sons: the first one also baptised William in 1631, the year after the King's son Charles was born and little Thomas a few years later. We all lived together in the large, roomy old house at Broom Hall, taking our part in farming the land, so it might have been that William would have lived the uneventful life of a country yeoman, with his wife and children.

Sadly, my brother Edward died when he was still a young man, so I took on the running of the estate, and in 1638 I married a wife, Margaret Dearn. Farming always suited me well, but William was never content to have a quiet and humdrum life. He was always much taken up with the affairs of Government and the conflicts of religion in our land. Many a time he would come back from a ride to Wolverhampton, to tell us of the latest troubles between the King and Parliament. When Charles I entered the House of Commons, attempting to have five members arrested, but discovered the "birds had flown" and left London to prepare for civil war, William talked about it in our parlour for many hours, in a mood of excitement and passion, speculating on the actions to come. My wife and I, and indeed Dorothy, were alarmed and fearful at the prospect of war, but William was stirred up to champion the King's cause, eager to fight to save us from the iron grip of Puritanism. He was determined to raise some troops and he soon joined the regiment of Thomas Leveson, a Catholic gentleman of Wolverhampton, who was a commander for His Majesty the King, in Staffordshire. In that summer of '42, he put me in charge of the harvest, kissed goodbye to Dorothy and his boys, and rode away, his heart full of enthusiasm, longing to take part in the gathering conflict.

[The sturdy yeoman stepped back into the shadows at the edge of the room, gesturing with a polite, deferential bow to the tall Cavalier, who now strode forward purposefully to face Ellen. This gentleman had an air of authority, as someone used to giving orders and being obeyed. She found herself listening respectfully to him as if he were delivering a military report from a battlefield, in his loud, strident voice.]

CHAPTER 2

Testimony of Colonel Thomas Leveson, a Royal Commander

When His Majesty Charles I raised his standard at Nottingham, on 22 August 1642, I was ready and willing to play my part in supporting and defending him from his pernicious enemies. In April of that year, when it had become clear the disagreements between the King and his Parliament might come to fighting, I had visited my armourer John Tanner in Wolverhampton to gather my weapons but was told by the unworthy fellow that Sir Walter Wrottesley had ordered him not to restore my arms to me and that I would need permission from the deputy lieutenant to claim them. As the fool of an armourer continued to deny me my weapons I shouted at the knave, laying about him with my cane and I must admit, raised a lump upon his forehead! For this Sir Wrottesley described me as an active and dangerous recusant; which words I hear with pride rather than the insult it was meant to be.

Along with other Catholic gentry, I began raising a regiment of fifteen hundred men in Staffordshire. John Biddulph lodged troops at Biddulph Hall and that remarkable, doughty Lady Isabel of Stafford, an obstinately staunch Catholic, garrisoned Stafford Castle. Other leading Catholics who supported the Royalist cause were

Christopher Heveningham of Pype Hall near Lichfield, William Fitzherbert of Swynnerton and young Walter Fowler, who it was said was often seen "with his sword by his side and his pole-axe in his hand".

William Careless came from Broomhall, in that part of Staffordshire near my town of Wolverhampton which had many Catholic families, including the Whitgreaves of Moseley and the wealthy Giffards of Chillington. My own family had intermarried a few times with the Giffards, for instance Joyce Leveson was the wife of John Giffard, that obstinate recusant who endured much tribulation during the time of the austere Queen Elizabeth. All these ancient Catholic families were more likely to side with the King, with his moderate Anglicanism and his Catholic wife, than with the Parliamentarians who, it was feared, would bring in a harsh form of Puritanism.

William Careless showed such skill and enthusiasm that I soon appointed him Captain of a troop in my newly formed regiment. I was given the rank of Colonel by the King and appointed governor of Dudley Castle, being authorised to levy troops from the inhabitants of Seisdon and Cuttlestone for a garrison at the castle. I raised provisions, money, beds with sheets, blankets, bolsters, teams to carry materials and men with tools to work on fortifications at the castle. This made me somewhat unpopular with the local people who found my levies a heavy and expensive burden, but being responsible for both Dudley Castle, and commander of the Royalist forces in the south-east and central Staffordshire, I felt it my bounden duty to fortify the castle strongly.

Eight miles away from Wolverhampton, Chillington Hall, an ancient Catholic house, was garrisoned for the King by Peter Giffard, who was then in his early sixties. In August 1643 Sir William Brereton, that most competent Parliamentary commander, marched from Stafford to attack it and breaching its defences soon occupied the house. When I heard that Mr Peter Giffard, his two sons and about eighty others, including a priest, had been taken prisoner, I was determined to retake the house; six weeks later I recaptured it and the King gave orders that it should be regarrisoned. I believe that the Giffards and the Careless family had been associated for generations, living in the same neighbourhood and the Carelesses being tenants of the Giffards.

Christopher Heveningham was a captain in the garrison at Chillington in September of 1643 and he, hearing that thirty loads of wheat were being sent to Sir William Brereton to supply his troops with food, from his wife's house at Weston-Under-Lizard, decided to attack the convoy and captured them.

After this small but satisfying victory, I then ordered Captain Heveningham to attack Lapley House, which he did on the shortest day of the year, 21 December, 1643. He captured Lapley and sent eighty prisoners to Chillington. William Careless had proved himself so capable, brave, resourceful and supremely loyal, that he was appointed captain of the garrison at Lapley House, which suited him well, for it was only a few miles from his home at Broomhall.

In April of the next year he was made governor of Tong Castle, which was in Shropshire just over the border with Staffordshire, about five miles from Careless' home. However, he did not stay there long for soon he was to travel further north. When Prince Rupert, the King's nephew sought to relieve the siege at York, Careless re-joined my regiment to support the Prince, and he was one of the captains involved with the taking of Bolton on 28 May 1644.

This action came to be called the Massacre of Bolton; certainly, there was fierce fighting and many were killed, but I doubt the numbers were as great as the Parliament side claimed in their propaganda news sheets. Prince Rupert was marching towards York to relieve the siege there and had taken the town of Stockton.

The Parliamentary commander Sir Alexander Rigby retired to Bolton, which was full of so many Puritans that it was called "The

Geneva of the North"; four regiments of soldiers were ordered to attack the town by the Prince, who did not realize fully how well defended the town was. A second attack was led by the Earl of Derby, young James Stanley.

The Royalists, many of whom were recruited from the Lancashire Catholic community, were infuriated by an incident whereby Colonel Shuttleworth, a Parliament defender, had allowed the hanging of an Irish Catholic. The Lancashire soldiers felt this was an affront to their religion. The walls of the town were stormed and the fighting was carried into the streets in a prolonged, brutal and bloody fashion. It was claimed that sixteen hundred defenders and inhabitants were slain.

Later, church registers would show that only seventy-eight townspeople were killed, and it may be excused that it was difficult in a battle in the streets to tell who of them were soldiers and who were innocent civilians. However, it must be admitted that Prince Rupert and the Earl of Derby had been remiss in not restraining or checking their troops and the people of Bolton remembered these two men with bitterness. William Careless, I am sure, conducted himself with honour, because I never saw him act cruelly or unchivalrously in all the years that we fought alongside each other.

Prince Rupert went on to attack and capture Liverpool, and then headed toward York, joining with the Earl of Newcastle. On a bleak, windswept moor between York and Leeds his army met in battle with Parliament's Northern and Eastern armies, together with a Scots force under Lord Leven; however, it was a disastrous day for our cause and Marston Moor was a decisive victory for His Majesty's enemies.

Careless was there with his regiment, fighting as part of the right-wing cavalry under the command of Lord Byron. He survived the battle safely, only to be unfortunately captured a few months later in a skirmish with a Parliamentarian force near Wolverhampton. He was sent as a prisoner to High House in the town of Stafford, where I heard that he was being held in April 1645.

As the Civil War went on, I was away at many of the battles, fighting alongside my monarch; I appointed Lieutenant Colonel Beaumont to govern Dudley Castle in my absence. He proved unpopular with the local inhabitants because of his harsh ways, once reportedly threatening to burn down the houses in Dudley because the townspeople would not send up musicians for his party!

After our most calamitous defeat at the Battle of Naseby in Northamptonshire, in June of 1645, I returned to Dudley Castle and finding it vulnerable to enemy attack I attempted to strengthen it. Fearing that those who would besiege us had too much cover from the houses in Castle Street and Saint Edmund's church, I ordered that these should be demolished, but this proved as futile as it was unpopular. On 27 April 1646 the Parliamentarian troops began a siege and used the stones from the demolished buildings to construct siege works; after two weeks I was forced to surrender. Thank God their commander, Sir William Brereton was a fair-minded man and he gave safe passage to my garrison, which consisted of forty officers and three hundred men. The castle itself, which had stood above the small town of Dudley since the days of the Conqueror, was partly demolished by the orders of Parliament, so that it could not be used by Royalists again. Thus they dealt with many a fair castle throughout the land, destroying the heritage of England, as the previous vile Cromwell had dealt with our monasteries and nunneries, back in Henry VIII's time.

But I digress from my account of Captain William Careless. It is often so when I begin to reminisce about that most dreadful yet stirring time of Civil War. There was never a soldier I was gladder of at my side in battle. Skilled and courageous, he would obey orders implicitly, yet he was also able to make his own decisions quickly and wisely. I was sorry to hear of his imprisonment, but then I believe he either escaped or was released, and the last I heard of him he had gone in exile to Ireland.

* * *

[It seemed quiet in the darkening room as the Royalist Commander stopped speaking abruptly. He swept a courteous bow to Ellen with an old-fashioned grace, then taking a pace back, he offered a supporting arm to the gentle looking lady, who came forward hesitantly and modestly. She spoke in a slow, soft manner, gaining confidence after a few moments.]

CHAPTER 3

Testimony of Dorothy Careless, wife of Colonel William Carlos

I am proud to acknowledge that I am the wife of Colonel William Carlos, although many times, being married to him has brought troubles and difficulties. My father was Walter Fox, a gentleman of Salt, which is a small village four miles from Stafford. I was baptised in Saint Leonard's church at Marston nearby, on 8th February 1609; two years later my brother Richard was born and then my brother William when I was five. There followed my beloved sister Elizabeth, then Katherine and my well-known brother Sampson.

When I married William Careless of Broom Hall, I knew he was a man who loved action and dreamed of adventure, but we were living at a modest yeoman's estate in a remote part of the Staffordshire countryside, far from the busy places of men, so I thought that we would lead a quiet life of farming and that eventually his restless nature would settle.

We sadly buried a baby son, but in 1631, the year after the King's wife Henrietta Maria was delivered of her son Charles, our beloved William was born. He was always a good and loving child, who was inspired by his father. We quietly practised our Catholic Faith, although it was not always easy to do so. To attend Mass, we had to secretly go to remote chapels, such as White Ladies or Black Ladies, or to the private house of some Catholic gentry, such as the Giffards' great house at Chillington, or occasionally a six miles ride to Moseley where the Whitgreaves maintained and secretly sheltered a priest. Sometimes my son was able to benefit from more advanced teaching through the generosity of Mr. Whitgreave, who allowed him to visit and share lessons from the tutor he employed for his nephews. As the tutor was really the priest in disguise, one John Huddleston, I was glad that William could also learn some of the doctrines and prayers of our Catholic Faith.

Our second dear son was born in 1640 and we named him Thomas in memory of one of William's ancestors who had leased the farm of Broomhall back in the reign of Henry VIII. A few months later, when war between His Sovereign Majesty Charles I and his Parliament was being threatened, William and I were noted on a list of recusants. Because of fines and limitations our finances were brought into a poor state but our Faith was precious to us and we could not tell a lie when asked directly about our beliefs.

In that fateful August of 1642, when the King declared his intention to fight his opponents, my husband entered into a state of mind of high excitement and eagerness for action. I was anxious, filled with foreboding of what might come. But I dursn't voice my fears to him; this was the noble cause for which he had dreamt of fighting, to defend the king with whom there was more hope of tolerance for our Faith than under the rule of those harsh men who would enforce stricter laws to vanquish it. John, his brother, tried to persuade him to stay quiet at home, avoiding danger, working at our estate of Broom Hall, but William heeded him not. I only urged him to take care, to write to me and come back safely to us whenever he could and concealed my trembling and tears. Our son William, now twelve years old, gazed at his father in his fine soldier's outfit with admiration and declared his wish to go with him.

My husband rode away down that green, leafy Staffordshire lane and I was left wondering, like ten thousand other wives, what would become of him in the weeks and months to come. It was as well I did not know then that it would be years of danger, injury, imprisonment, weary exile and separation before the civil strife in England would be over.

He wrote to me to inform me that he was raising troops to join the regiment of Colonel Leveson and his letters were very full of zeal and enthusiasm for this work. Meanwhile my life at Broom Hall continued quietly; I was occupied with teaching my son William what I could in the way of reading and writing and caring for my baby Thomas. I gained great comfort from the good company of my sister-in-law Margaret and her ever growing number of children.

William gained leave from his duties with Colonel Leveson to come home to see me and our sons. The visit was very short, as there was much to do forming the regiment, and fighting was breaking out throughout England. He was soon away again, helping Thomas Leveson to organise his troops.

Because of our remote situation we were somewhat sheltered from the troubles of the war, but from time to time we would learn of confrontations and violence. So it was that we heard in the August of 1643 that Parliamentary troops had marched from Stafford, led by Sir William Brereton, to attack Chillington Hall. We were sorry and alarmed to hear that our good old friend Peter Giffard was a prisoner, along with many others who had been garrisoned at his house, including the priest. It was a great relief to us that a few weeks later, Christopher Heveningham led a Royalist force to rescue and retake Chillington.

Having re-occupied the house, from there he sent a force to seize supplies of wheat that were being sent to help feed the Parliamentary troops. Encouraged by his success with that action, he was sent by my husband's commander, Colonel Leveson to attack Lapley House, which lies only a few miles from our home. Just before Christmas, we heard that Heveningham had taken Lapley village, sent eighty prisoners to be held at Chillington and that my husband was going to be placed in charge at Lapley. I was very glad at this news because he would be so close to us. A few times I went with John to visit him there and I was much pleased with Lapley village, which is a pleasant place.

I was even more proud and pleased when William was appointed governor of Tong Castle in April 1644. This fine edifice belonged to William Pierrepoint, a gentleman who later became known as "William the Wise", because of his skill at negotiating between King Charles I and Parliament, when his Majesty was held prisoner on the Isle of Wight. Mr. Pierrepoint lived away in Nottinghamshire during the war and had a difficult family situation because one son was for the King but the other son supported Parliament. The castle had been held by the enemy, but in February 1644 they were forced to quit; however, they burned and did much damage before they left, to the castle, the church and the College nearby, so that when William took over it was in a sorry state, needing repairs.

As Tong is also just a few miles from our home, just over the border into the county of Salop, I hoped that he might spend the rest of the war there, but in May, I was much alarmed to hear that he was going to march north, to assist Prince Rupert, the King's nephew, who was advancing on York. It was certain there would be a large battle, the most serious fighting that William had faced so far.

Every day and every night I prayed for him and his men, often holding my sweet babe, who slept unknowing and untroubled, while the tears ran down my face. Young William enquired eagerly each day if there was any news of his father's actions, looking out for any visitors to the house who might bring news. Richard, one of the Penderel family, brought me a letter one day, which was stained by being passed along through many hands. It was from my beloved husband, who was triumphant that Bolton was now in Royalist hands but lamented that so many ordinary and innocent townspeople had died. He wished for better discipline and restraint among the troops.

A few weeks later in July, the fearful news came that the Royalists had suffered a most dreadful defeat at Marston Moor, near York. For a while I was in despair, thinking he must surely have been killed, but after a most anxious time, he made his way back to us, weary, weak and in most disappointed spirits. I half hoped he might then give up this life of soldiering, but soon his determination and courage recovered and he was away again to help Colonel Leveson to the utmost of his ability. Such is the quality of this man who is my true and faithful spouse.

I tried my utmost not to fret or worry, but my heart sank when in December a messenger came to inform me, that he had been involved in a skirmish near Wolverhampton and was now a prisoner of the Parliamentarian troops.

For a while we did not know where he was held, and indeed he may have been taken from place to place, but in April the next spring, in 1645, we received information that he was being held a prisoner at Stafford, at High House.

It is a long journey to Stafford from Broomhall, about twelve miles, so that even with a good, sound horse it took myself and John about three hours to travel there, but I was determined to visit him, as we had not seen one another for months. As we rode into the town I remembered many occasions when I had been there with my father in my girlhood, for Salt is not far from Stafford. Now I saw how many houses and buildings had been damaged during the war; the castle had been held at first by Lady Stafford, but then in 1643 the Parliamentarians had taken the town, established a committee to control the area, and assigned the High House to accommodate any Royalist prisoners who were of some rank or status.

My heart lifted when I saw High House, for it is truly a fine building, built at the end of the last century by the Dorrington family, who were a wealthy and respected family. At the time when the war began, the Sneyd family were renting the house, and they had

The Ancient High House in Stafford.

welcomed His Majesty the King and Prince Rupert to stay two nights there, as they were marching towards Shrewsbury, in the September of 1642. There was much decorative timber, many windows and the upper storeys hung out over the street, showing how large the rooms were. "Surely," I thought, "my husband will be kept comfortably here?"

Indeed, as we entered in and were shown the upstairs, we met him in a well-furnished, spacious room, overlooking the street. He strode across to embrace me eagerly and I held on to him for several moments, before beginning to ask him some of the thousand questions that were in my mind. I perceived him to be worn and tense, older than when we had parted, as though he had borne suffering and anxiety, but he asked with the old accustomed liveliness about the children and the farm.

"And are you comfortable here, William? It seems a handsome place, but do they treat you well?" He laughed at my concern.

"We have good food and good wine and are treated like gentlemen. I may keep a servant, if I could afford it and we are allowed to go into the street and walk about, upon our word of honour not to escape. Last week, the weather being fine, I took a walk down by the River Sow, a pleasant stream. And being permitted to have visits from our wives is a great joy to us my dear, as with seeing yourself here today." Saying this he put his arm round me again, and held the other out to John, who stepped forward and grasped his hand with great emotion showing in his honest face.

"Indeed, it is good to see you again brother after so many months of not knowing what was happening to you," exclaimed John in a heartfelt manner. For several minutes the two of them talked, as men do, not so much of their emotions but of practical affairs, of the state of the farm, the price of wheat, the prospects of fair weather for the harvest and the difficulties of employing reliable workers. When questioned, William told us a little of the action he had seen and how he was captured, but I felt he hid a good deal, not wanting to relive the horrors of battles, or the suffering from wounds and captivity, or add to my heartache.

"And here you are now," teased John, "dwelling at ease in a house fit for a gentleman!"

"Fit indeed for a king!" replied William laughing, and he narrated to us the story of how the King and his nephew Rupert had been accommodated at the house and used it for meeting with their captains and planning their strategy for the War, which at that date had recently begun. William showed us on the stair the window through which we could see the tower of St. Mary's church, and was much amused by the anecdote that the rather enthusiastically rash young Prince had been showing off a new type of rifle and fired it at the church steeple, damaging the top of it. To my mind, though I kept it close in my private thoughts, I was perturbed to think of a young man finding naught but amusement from a new gun, heedless of the many lives that would be lost or ruined in this sorry war.

Tentatively I asked, "William, do you know what will happen to you now? Are you to be kept here for the rest of the war, however long that may be?" At this his dear face became serious once more.

"There are rumours that I and the other officers imprisoned here may be sent into exile, perhaps to Ireland, where we can do little harm. We would be honour bound not to return to England, on pain of death if we do try to re-join the King's army. We have been treated well thus far, but the Parliamentary forces cannot spare the soldiers to guard us indefinitely. So, my dear, you will have to be brave and face awhile without me again, and I cannot say whether it will be for weeks or months."

"Or years!" I cried bitterly and at this last cruel blow, I could not hold back my emotions any longer but clung to him and wept, while John looked down at his feet or out of the window, his plain countryman's face working with the effort of keeping his self-control.

"Calm yourself, dear Dorothy. We must find strength in the Lord to bear these difficult trials and trust in Him that our Cause will prevail and that we will be together again in not too distant a time. I will write to you often, and you have our dear sons to keep you occupied, and our trusted brother John and his sweet Margaret will support you and care for you."

So spoke my brave husband, attempting to console me, all the while holding me to him and stroking my hair. John stepped closer towards us adding his own comforting words.

"Indeed, Dorothy, you need not fear that you or your sons will be in want, for there is always a place at Broom Hall for you; and Margaret says you are a great help to her with managing the house and the children. It may not be long until the King's fortunes improve and then we will welcome William home again, before you know it."

Seeing their concern for me, I pretended to put away my grief, dried my tears and spoke calmly and courageously to them both. I reassured William that I would take care of our sons and keep a cheerful countenance for their sake, and I thanked John for his brotherly kindness to our family. As fate turned out, I was right to be fearful, for from that time on the fortunes of the King declined even more; disastrous defeats were inflicted on His Majesty leading to his imprisonment, trial and his most dreadful execution. Fortunate it was that, at that moment, the future was hidden from us.

All too soon, our visit was at an end. A Roundhead soldier came into the room and bade us, not too harshly, to say our farewells, before accompanying us out to the busy street once more. In silence, too full of sadness to speak, John and I mounted our horses and rode back to the seclusion of Broom Hall. It was years before I saw William again.

The Cavalier's Wife

Oh do not go, my dear husband,
My heart will break without you.
Let our quiet lives in this secluded place
In mutual love continue.
Our children safe within our arms
Our family dwelling in God's Grace.

Dear Dorothy, my dearest wife,
I fear that I must leave you.
To defend the King on busy battlefield.
But my heart's thoughts will be at all times with you.
Our precious Faith I must fight for
Or to harsh Puritan masters yield.

If I go not, my two dear sons
Will ask ashamed about me,
"Why did our father cowardly stay at home,
Not struggle for liberty?
Not strive to pray as once we did
Our forefathers dwelling in God's Grace?"

[Dorothy had become more emotional as she remembered that difficult time and tears flowed quietly down her cheeks as she turned back to her place. Ellen felt she wanted to reach out and put a comforting hand on her shoulder, but there was no time as the other Royalist Officer advanced decisively with all the assurance and presence of an honourable gentleman. The pride of generations was apparent on his countenance as he began his testimony.]

CHAPTER 4

Testimony of Charles Giffard, a member of the Royalist Army at the Battle of Worcester

I belong to an ancient and noble family, which came over to England with William the Conqueror in 1066. Since the twelfth century our home has been at Chillington near Brewood in Staffordshire. My ancestor Thomas Giffard acquired the estate of the convent of Black Ladies during the reign of Henry VIII and this, together with White Ladies, and Boscobel has been a refuge of the Old Catholic Faith for the inhabitants of Staffordshire, for gentry, yeomen and labourers, all during the times of persecution and recusancy. Indeed, our family also owned Broom Hall, with Sir John Lane and leased it to the Careless family, so I knew William Careless as one of our tenants.

The Giffard family motto is "Prenez haleine, tirez fort" which means, "Take breath, pull strong". The story goes that Sir John Giffard, during the reign of Henry VIII, was out hunting when he saw a panther, which having escaped from his private collection of exotic animals, was about to leap upon a woman and her child. Sir John drew an arrow to aim at the panther, and his son standing nearby uttered those words to help him, "Take breath and pull strong". The shot was successful and the woman and her child were saved.

To my mind the motto describes our family most aptly. We are strong and determined in our holding to the Faith of our Fathers, and we do not let the difficulties of circumstances make us waver from our beliefs.

My great grandfather, John Giffard, held to his faith in the Catholic Church through times of threats and persecution during the reign of Queen Elizabeth, though to my mind, it seems he was wily and adept at escaping the worst punishments. When Her Majesty made a royal progress through the county of Staffordshire, she stayed one night at his newly built house at Chillington, and it must have come to her notice that he did not attend the Church of England service in the village of Brewood, because a short time later he was summoned with other Staffordshire gentry, to appear before the Privy Council to explain why they did not come to church. They admitted their defaulting, "alleging their consciences and the example of their forefathers who taught them so". They were told they would not be allowed home unless they obeyed the Queen's laws, but my great grandfather, who was at this time a Justice of the Peace, was allowed to go back to Chillington to put the house in order, as long as he returned to be in the custody of the Bishop of Rochester.

Later, in November, some of the other Recusants were being put into prison in London; family friends of ours, Brian Fowler was sent to the Fleet and Sampson Erdeswick was sent to the Marshalsea. However, our great grandfather was willing to compromise, and was allowed to go home, having promised to attend the parish church at Brewood. He played it craftily, pointing out that he was not able to go every Sunday or holy day as the church was a mile and a half away from Chillington, thus gaining permission from the Privy Council to hold prayers for himself and his family at the chapel in his house.

Who knows how many Catholic Masses were said there, sustaining the Old Faith of his family, tenants and neighbours?

Again in 1580, John Giffard appeared before the Privy Council and was sent to the Marshalsea Prison, but was released a few weeks later because of his health, provided that he lived in or around London. For a while he took a house in St Helen's parish, and lived there under house arrest; the next summer he was given permission to go to the new wells at Newnham Regis in Warwickshire for fourteen days and to his manor at Marston near Stafford for eight days.

When the Spanish Armada threatened England, and Catholics were very much regarded with suspicion and dread, my great grandfather was again in danger of arrest, but he was treated leniently in view of his generally law-abiding character, although one malicious person referred to him as, "the most double, treble villain that ever lived"! He was placed under the custody of Thomas Phelippes, one of the agents of that foul man Francis Walsingham, Elizabeth's Machiavellian spymaster. Phelippes held two-thirds of our estates which had been sequestered under the recusancy penalties. Four years later he was still being guarded by Phelippes and had to appear yet again before Staffordshire justices along with several other gentry from the area including Sampson Erdeswick, Edward Stanford of Perry Hall in Handsworth, and Humphrey Comberford. Some who failed to appear such as Brian Fowler and members of the Macclesfield family and the Draycott family were arrested and sent to be detained in the Bishop's Palace at Lichfield.

Although he spent much of his life in custody or house arrest, and had some of his property sequestered, John Giffard retained enough wealth to contribute to the shire hall in Stafford and to be buried in a fine tomb in the church of Saint Mary in Brewood, alongside his wife Joyce and with carved figures of their fourteen children.

I relate all this to you so that you may understand that in our county around Brewood we had a tradition of hiding from persecution and arrest. It needed much loyalty and ability to keep secrets and to continue the practice of our religion, and we all knew the trustworthiness of each family. My family built hiding places into their houses so that priests could survive; persecution only seemed to make our Faith grow stronger. My father Peter Giffard had sisters who were nuns and five daughters who became nuns. My cousin Bonaventure Giffard was a priest, educated in Douai and Paris.

When the war against the first King Charles began my father Peter (though getting on in years) made every effort to raise troops and to garrison Chillington in order to support the Royalist side. For this he suffered much, for the house was attacked in 1643 and we became prisoners for a while. I was a young man at this time, only twenty-two when our family home was occupied by the Parliamentarians. My father was imprisoned at Stafford and then at Eccleshall Castle and we heard that the demolition of Chillington had been ordered. However, my brother Walter's wife Anne was given permission to live in the house with her two children and two servant maids in February 1645 and in the April, my father was released and given permission to live back at his home, provided that he promised not to take up arms again, for which he paid a large security of £165 deposit and another £65 every quarter of a year up to Christmas.

The heavy cost of the war to my father was not only monetary; he paid a heavier price in the loss of kinsmen. His dear brother Andrew of Wolverhampton died in a skirmish near that town and Francis Giffard of Water Eaton in Penkridge, who was a royalist captain, died in fighting near Dudley.

It seemed that all our hopes were at an end when the King's forces were defeated and the King himself was shamefully executed in January 1649. His son Charles was only nineteen, though he had taken part in many battles in support of his father. The young Prince went abroad, and I heard that our good friend William Careless was also in exile in Ireland then Spain, but he secretly returned to the Staffordshire area in 1649. He was forced abroad again, this time taking his oldest son William with him to the Low Countries.

When His Majesty Charles II decided to return to England, gathering an army in Scotland, it was rumoured locally that Colonel Careless slipped back again into England with his son and lived for about nine months very quietly and discreetly in the area of Brewood, waiting to join the King's army.

In late August 1651, Careless raised a small number of recruits and enlisted in the cavalry troop of the Earl of Shrewsbury, Lord Talbot, where he served as a Major. I too, with my loyal servant Francis Yates and many others from our area, was ready to join the King, as we heard that he was planning to march from Scotland, down through England on his way to London. We hoped to overthrow the tyrant Cromwell and restore our rightful monarch.

After spending some frustrating and tedious months in Scotland, becoming weary of the demands of the Presbyterians there, and under threat from Cromwell's forces, Charles had decided to leave Stirling and march south into England, thinking that large numbers of Royalists would rally to his cause and join with his army. We heard unconfirmed reports that the King's forces consisted of about four thousand horse and dragoons and also nine thousand foot soldiers; but many English were suspicious of his Scottish troops, and doubtful of success against the well-organized Parliamentary militia. Instead of the thousands, that he expected, only hundreds of his supporters joined him.

Charles came to Carlisle and was proclaimed King, but at the same time the Parliamentary Council of State was ordering the County militias of Yorkshire, Lancashire and Cheshire to be ready to block the King's way; added to this, four thousand Parliamentary

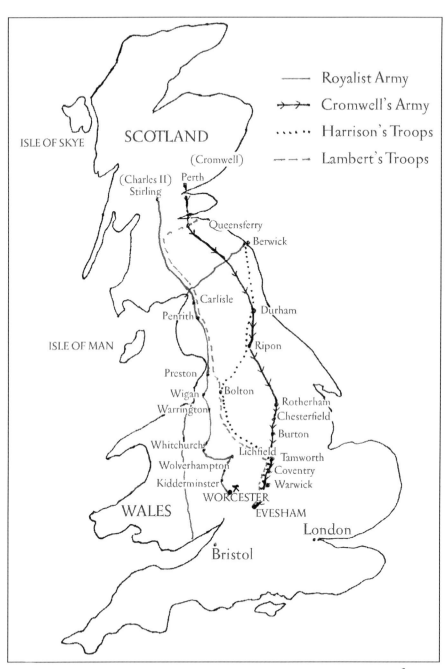

Map of the movements of the Cavalier and Parliamentary troops towards Worcester.

men under Major General Harrison marched west from Berwick on the east coast. Hurrying down from Scotland Major General Lambert with three thousand horse and dragoons detached from Cromwell's army. These two formidable forces threatened the Royal Army's progress, like a great game of chess where the knights close in to entrap the King.

I was looking forward eagerly to joining with the King's army as he drew near to Staffordshire, but every day we heard fresh reports about Parliament calling up militia to stop him reaching London, gathering at Northampton, Saint Albans and Gloucester. The King was being impeded, with a view to surrounding him and rendering him unable to move. Most to be feared was Cromwell himself, with his deadly disciplined army of veterans hurrying southwards down the east side of England.

We Staffordshire Royalists thought that when His Majesty came to our county many recruits would join him but such was not the case. One night his army camped at Blore Heath, near Market Drayton, at which time he had about six thousand horse and seven thousand foot soldiers, but the men were in poor condition after so many days of marching. A summons for shoes and other necessities was made to the town of Nantwich but was refused and the town of Shrewsbury also refused to surrender or help.

When he realized that I was full of zeal to join up, my father remonstrated with me, pleading with me not to go to battle again. "Has not our family given and suffered enough?" he asked me. "You are my youngest son and if we should lose you, it will bring despair in my old age. These last few peaceful years have given us some respite and I dread to take up the fighting once again." But I persuaded him and heartened him, reminding him of his own strength of spirit in the early days of this dispute against the Monarchy, and with some reluctance he gave me his blessing to depart and promised his prayers for my safety.

The King's army continued south towards London, and came, utterly exhausted, on 22 August, to Worcester where Charles hoped to find rest and supplies for his troops. It was a city which was proud of its loyalty to the Royal house and had a good defensive situation, being situated on the River Severn. As I rode into the centre of Worcester, I saw the broad meadows which lie near the magnificent Cathedral, thronged with a great assembly of people whom the King was addressing. But listening to him, I felt that many of the people were not in accord with the Religious Settlement that he was proposing, which was based on the strict Scottish Covenant. He had been forced to agree to a deal with the harshly Calvinistic Scots but Englishmen preferred their more moderate Anglican Church; nor were they convinced by his promise of an Act of Oblivion, offering pardon to those who had fought against him if he should win government. Who knew if promises of future mercy would be kept?

At least they seemed reassured when he promised that the Scots would return to their own country, but when he tried to order a levy of men between the ages of sixteen and sixty to fight with him, he met with little response. The news of Cromwell's army, rumoured to be up to thirty thousand experienced soldiers, rapidly drawing near to Worcester, whereas His Majesty had only about sixteen thousand weary troops, made men wary of joining the side that might lose.

Over the next two weeks it became increasingly clear that our position was weak and dangerous. Cromwell and his troops advanced with menacing haste, his men "jogging in their shirt sleeves" in the August heat, and every day we heard more news of him threatening to close off our way to London; by 27 August he had arrived at Evesham, thirteen miles south-east of Worcester. Knowing what a skilled general he was, we realized he would aim to also cut off any escape route to Wales by occupying the River Severn.

His Majesty showed great leadership at this desperate time, in preparing defences for the city in which we now felt ourselves to be surrounded. He ordered the blowing up of four bridges which gave vital access to the town, and the Scots army were set to make strong a hill overlooking the Cathedral, named then Fort Royal; three regiments of Scots were set to guard where the River Severn met the River Teme in the fields below the city to the west. The very streets of Worcester were filled with soldiers. Even so, we felt how difficult things were for us, and in our hearts, we resonated with the words of the brave Duke of Hamilton:

> "I cannot tell ...whether our hopes or fears are greatest, but we have one stout argument-despair; for we must either stoutly fight or die."

A great blow was dealt to us on the 28th day of August when we heard that the Parliamentary troops had managed to get across the River Severn at Upton, nine miles south of Worcester. It was thought that the bridge there had been demolished, but by some strange mismanagement a plank had been left across, which eighteen of Lambert's Parliamentary dragoons swiftly took advantage of, followed by many more men. They repaired the bridge and by the end of the day nearly twelve thousand enemy troops had crossed, nearly as many as our entire army. Our brave General Massey, who had served us so well at Gloucester, was disabled by several wounds he received while desperately trying to stem the tide of intruders.

The Parliamentary commanders, who it must be acknowledged were extremely skilled in their strategy, then ordered the building of twenty pontoons to form two floating bridges across the rivers Severn and Teme, which made it easy for Parliamentary troops to pour across. At the same time, Cromwell was moving up, to encircle us on the East side of the city and his artillery began to fire at our defences.

Even so, when we thought he would immediately attack, Cromwell waited. I believe he was letting our fears build up to weary our spirits;

it suited him also to delay until the third of September, a date which had been so auspicious for him at the battle of Dunbar the previous year, and so disastrous for us. The King spent these days tirelessly planning strategies, consulting with his commanding officers, pleading with the Scots troops and encouraging his English supporters. Although he was a young man compared to Cromwell, that seasoned veteran, Charles showed great leadership and courage throughout the action at Worcester. Every day we would meet at his Commandery where the Duke of Hamilton had set up headquarters. This was a large, rambling, ancient house which three centuries before had been a hospital and in Tudor times had been lived in by a rich merchant family. Where monks had once tended to the sick and thereafter wealthy people had dined and danced merrily, we would discuss how to defend the loyal city of Worcester from its dreadful danger.

We were further discouraged when on the last day of August, the Earl of Derby arrived, tired and dispirited after his defeat at Wigan. It had been hoped he would bring larger numbers to support us, but he had lost many, killed or injured, in that disastrous fray, with four hundred taken prisoner as well as dozens of officers. Most of the one hundred and seventy soldiers he had recruited from the Isle of Man were either slain on the battlefield or hunted down through the hedges and lanes. Lord Derby had been wounded and forced to flee; he and Colonel Roscarrock had hidden for a few days near my home in Staffordshire, at a small hunting lodge called Boscobel. Now they came to join us at Worcester, with only about thirty horsemen.

At this time, I found that Colonel William Careless was a source of strength to us all, with his unwavering, sense of purpose, brave spirits and firm loyalty to His Majesty. I was glad to be with him again, as he was a familiar face from my own part of the country, and he had such long experience of war and battles that he brought wisdom and knowledge to the decisions to be made. His young son William, who was the same age as the King, was with him, and I remember thinking it must have been hard for Dorothy, to see her husband and son riding away together to war.

The horrors of that battle still create a dark place in my soul. Such bitter, final failure after such great hopes of vanquishing at last the Parliamentary enemy, caused desperation for all of us who had risked everything to serve our King.

The day dawned fine and clear, but the alarm was raised when firing was heard from the south-west where the Parliamentary Leader General Fleetwood was leading two columns from Upton upon Severn towards the flood plain of the River Teme below Worcester. King Charles climbed the tower of the Cathedral to survey the situation, in his buff coat and boots, red sash and the George about his neck, and through his spy glass he could see the bridge of boats being towed up the River Severn to cross it, as well as most of Cromwell's cavalry who had moved into position to support General Fleetwood. The King realized that there would be fewer troops now to the south-east and decided to order a charge out of the Sudbury gate; he himself joined in the fray which seemed at first to be successful. For three hours he fought alongside his men, shouting words of encouragement, and for a while the enemy's troops fell back. If only Leslie, the General of the Scots troops had joined in then, I believe the day may have been ours, such was the zeal and energy of those Royalists with the King; but Leslie was either undecided, or fearful of losing all his men.

Maybe he thought that it would be better to save his Scots army for another time or try to bring them safely back to Scotland. Whatever it was, no help was forthcoming for us hard pressed Royalists. We were running out of ammunition and many men had to fight using the heavy butt end of their muskets as clubs, rather than firing them.

Though we on our side were not helped by Leslie, the Parliamentary troops from the Essex and Cheshire militia that we were fighting, some of whom were inexperienced in combat, were rallied and heartened by Cromwell and his veterans coming to their aid. Soon could be heard the battle shouts of "Lord of Hosts!" as they hurled themselves upon us, and we, being exhausted, were forced to retreat.

Now indeed there was crush and confusion around the Sudbury gate as the Royalists tried to go back into the city, hastened into a panic as Cromwell's troops, having captured Fort Royal from us, turned the guns towards us and fired into the town and at our retreating soldiers. The King himself was nearly trapped in Sudbury, but for the quick thinking of a fellow called Bagnall, who pushed an ammunition wagon between His Majesty and those pursuing him.

Having got back into the city, I heard the King riding up and down the street, shouting and calling his men in an effort to rally them, but in vain. David Leslie's troops seemed in a state of confusion and could not be persuaded to charge with the King. Reports came from every direction of the enemy entering the town from the west and from the east, so that panic set in amongst our horse soldiers, who were riding into each other and ready to cut each other's throats in their terror.

I was involved in fierce hand to hand combat all down the street, along with dozens of others, and at one strange, memorable moment, a door of one of the houses opened, and a young girl of about nine or ten, ventured out upon her doorstep. Her eyes went wide with wonder as she saw the gutter of the road running red with blood from the slaughtered soldiers. Her mother appeared behind her, screamed in fear and snatched the little maid back into the house, slamming and bolting the door. Methinks that girl would remember that sight all her life and recount it in her old age to her grandchildren, and they to theirs.

With the taste of defeat bitter in our mouths, it was realized that the very life of the King was in danger, and so action must be taken to bring him out of the battle and away from the city. He must escape if there was ever going to be any chance of his eventual success. He was unwilling to leave the scene of battle but was at length prevailed upon, seeing it was the only course of action left to him. Lord Derby, Lord Wilmot and I rode close to him back to his lodgings in Berkeley House in the Corn Market, while the Earl of Cleveland, Colonel William Careless, and Sir William Hamilton with some other officers, to cover the King's retreat, bravely charged down Sudbury at the Parliamentary troops who were breaking through. They held it until General Fleetwood passed the River and came into the city from the west and Cromwell forced Sudbury Gate, putting the brave Earl of Cleveland and his gallant officers into retreat. At the house, His Majesty in great haste divested himself of his armour and slipped out of the back door, while Cromwell's troops were arriving at the front door. We headed north, through St. Martin's gate and left the ill-fated city of Worcester at about six in the evening.

A number of valiant Royalists remained in Worcester, some making a stand at the town hall, until they were overcome, and some at Castle Mound, which was a strong position, held by Lord Rothes; fighting continued until about ten o'clock, before Cromwell offered honourable terms which were accepted. I knew Colonel Careless and his son continued fighting in the city after the King had gone, and it was said afterwards that Careless witnessed the last death of the battle. I am not sure how he left the city, but he told me later he had become separated from his son and did not know for a while what had happened to him. It turned out that young William had headed towards London, but his father set out for his home in Staffordshire.

Fleeing from Worcester

Several times the King faced about, striving to rally the troops to continue the fight. Coming to a bridge at Barbourn Brook, about half a mile out of the city, the officers stopped to confer; but seeing many soldiers throwing down their arms and being set on escaping, it seemed the best course of action would be to concentrate on saving His Majesty. About sixty of the King's servants, nobles and officers joined to ride with him, and there was a great press of soldiers, who hindered our progress, for the Scottish cavalry of about three thousand men were also trying to escape that way; the King complained somewhat bitterly, that during the day he could not get them to fight for him, but now he could not get rid of them.

Those of us who rode with the king were desperate and fearful indeed, not knowing at first whither we were going, but only eager to depart from danger. After about five miles heading north of Worcester, we came to a small pleasant village called Ombersley,

Inn at Ombersley, where the King and his men stopped for refreshments.

where we stopped for a few minutes for some refreshments at the inn, as most of us, including the King, had not eaten or drunken for many hours, and we were exhausted and famished.

There was much debate and quarrelling about where the King should head for, some saying Scotland, and some Wales and the King himself favouring London. Lord Derby took the lead in deciding to head north, and in order to try to free ourselves from the numbers of Scots army we, the King's party, left the main road and branched off to the right, just past Hartlebury. Then on in haste through the fading evening light, we took the chance again to halt at Whittington Manor near Kinver, once the home of the grandfather of Dick Whittington, the famous mayor of London. A soldier from Lord Talbot's regiment was called upon to guide us, but as darkness fell the poor fellow became confused and confessed to us that he was lost.

It was at this point that I was called forward to advise the King and his close followers. His Majesty had been consulting with George Villiers, the Duke of Buckingham, the Earl of Derby and Lord Wilmot about where they might find a place to rest for a few hours. Some weeks before the fugitive Earl of Derby, desperate to hide from pursuing Parliamentary troops, had been hidden and sheltered by my family at Boscobel. He was impressed by the honesty and resourcefulness of our Catholic community, for we were of course well used to hiding refugees from the authorities. The King agreed to this suggestion, and asked Lord Talbot to tell his guide to lead us to Boscobel, but as Walker was not sure of the way, I offered my own servant, Francis Yates, who knew the local country well, to lead us on through the ever darkening, narrow lanes.

Francis, I knew, we could trust with our lives, an honest, reliable, knowledgeable fellow, whose family had served the Giffards well through many years. My own feelings were a mixture of immense pride at this chance to serve my monarch, deep anxiety about the tremendous responsibility for his safety, and great relief that we were returning to my own home and area.

Approaching Stourbridge, we discussed whether it was safe to go through that town, but feeling that it was the quickest way, we decided to speak only French, so that if anyone should overhear us, they would be less likely to realize we were in the company of the King. A few miles beyond that town, at a house at Wordsley, we stopped for something to eat, the King being hungry again, but

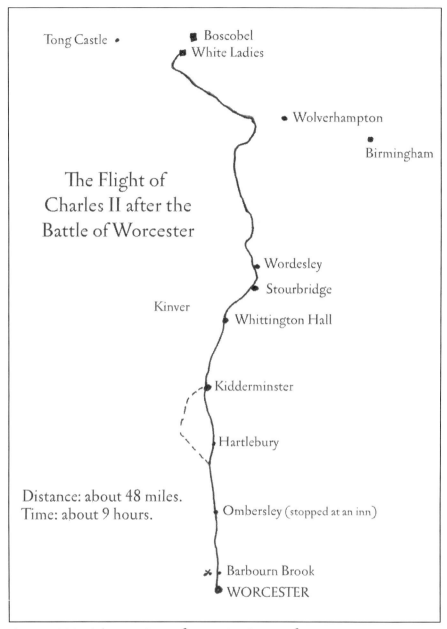

Tong Castle

Boscobel
White Ladies

Wolverhampton

Birmingham

The Flight of
Charles II after the
Battle of Worcester

Wordesley
Stourbridge

Kinver

Whittington Hall

Kidderminster

Hartlebury

Distance: about 48 miles.
Time: about 9 hours.

Ombersley (stopped at an inn)

Barbourn Brook
WORCESTER

A map of Charles' escape from Worcester heading to White Ladies in Staffordshire.
The dashed line shows where most of the Scottish troops went a different way.

there was not much to be had, only a crust of bread and some small beer.

As we rode on, the King began asking Colonel Roscarrock about Boscobel and how he could be securely hidden there, but I offered my humble opinion to them that it might be better to go to White Ladies first, another house owned by my family, about half a mile away from Boscobel, smaller and more secret. There we could rest, discuss what to do next and find out if it was safe to go on to Boscobel.

"What kind of house is this White Ladies?" enquired the King. "Tell me why it has such a pretty, romantic name?"

"Sire," I replied, "It was a priory for Augustinian nuns in former times, since, I believe from the year 1100, but in the Reformation, it was closed down and the few sisters who still lived there were scattered. There was a half-timbered house as part of the buildings, probably where the Prioress lived, and that house was sold to the Skeffington family and so passed after some years to my kinsman, John Giffard, through marriage. His widow Dorothy owns it now, but I think she may be away from home."

"My kinsman George Giffard is living there at the moment. There are a few servants, but they are all loyal and trustworthy; Mrs Anne Andrew the housekeeper will find you some food, Edward and Bartholomew Martin work in the woods and round the house, and George and John Penderel can be relied on to help you. They are from a family of five brothers who have served my family well through many years. All the family know how to be discreet and how to hide people."

I refrained from saying that it was Catholic priests that they were used to hiding, but I think His Majesty understood, for with a wry, half smile he asked no more, but merely said,

"Then let us press on and find this quiet, safe place, and these worthy Penderels, for I and my horse are both weary and hungry and are longing for a rest."

It was with a great feeling of relief, after seemingly endless hours of riding fearfully through pitch dark, winding roads, which seemed no more than overgrown paths, trusting always to the good common sense and years of experience of my trusty Francis that we came at last to the ancient walls of White Ladies House. I rode up the drive before the rest and with a sense that I was seeking sanctuary, like some poor travellers had in centuries before when it was a priory, I hammered loudly on the door.

Refuge at White Ladies

It was by now about three o'clock in the morning and George Penderel must have been alarmed at being woken by our knocking on the front door. He opened the window, looked out in alarm and saw nearly eighty weary soldiers on horseback. Quickly Francis Yates, his brother-in-law, called out to him and seeing me as well, George ran down in order to open the door to us.

"What news from Worcester?" he enquired anxiously.

"The King has been defeated and is in danger of his life," answered Yates urgently. "Quick, make haste and get dressed. We need shelter and rest for him and Mr. Giffard and all these others."

Not waiting for George to finish dressing, I led the King and most of the nobles into the house. Some of the lords and officers lay down exhausted on the beds, chairs or on the floor to rest for half an hour, and the servants and ordinary soldiers did the same, after having seen to the poor tired horses. But a few of us were again discussing urgently what to do next for the King's safety. The question still was whether he should slip over the Shropshire border and head for Wales, or continue north to Scotland, or try to ride back down south to London. One point that was swiftly agreed on was that most of the company must separate from His Majesty, such a large number of soldiers being very conspicuous; he would be safer on his own, or with only one or two companions.

I, knowing the most reliable men in the neighbourhood, sent for Richard Penderel, who lived nearby at Hobbal Grange. Colonel Roscarrock, who in company of Lord Derby had been helped and hidden a few weeks before by the local families, sent the young servant lad, Bartholomew Martin to Boscobel to bring William Penderel.

While we were waiting, it was agreed the King must be disguised. He took off the blue ribbon and diamond badge of the Order of the Garter and gave it to Colonel Blague to look after. How it grieved me to see him doing this so resignedly, when only the previous morning he had been putting it on to be a symbol and rallying sign to our troops. His distinctive long black curling hair was cut short by Lord Wilmot with a knife, and the king rubbed his hands on the back of the chimney, afterwards smearing his face with the soot, in order to make himself appear less clean and well cared for.

Richard Penderel came promptly, his brother William arriving not long after. They immediately grasped the importance and dangers of the situation, as I had known they would. I sent Richard back to find a suit of workman's clothes for the King and he returned quickly with a jerkin and breeches of green coarse cloth, and a doublet. A noggin shirt belonging to the servant boy Edward Martin, a grey hat of Humphrey Penderel's and some rough shoes from the servant lad William Creswell, were also provided by these generous men, whom I knew had little money compared to us, but were ready to give up anything in order to preserve the King.

I had sent George Penderel out to see if there were any fugitives or enemy troops in the area, and he came back with the news that the coast was clear at the moment, but there were some Parliamentary soldiers quartered at Codsall, only three miles away, and they would be awake, up and about and searching soon. William and Richard Penderel urged us to make haste; the house of White Ladies would not be safe for long.

White Ladies (at the front on the left-hand side) and Boscobel (through the woods near the back of the picture).

It was agreed that the King should hide in the woods nearby, and the rest of the company depart. As he prepared to part from his loyal band of supporters, his words of gratitude lifted our hearts and filled our souls with a renewed strength that our tired bodies so dearly craved, to sustain us during the long, hazardous days and nights ahead. At all times this past dreadful night he had remained brave and undaunted, even smiling with amusement at his newly acquired appearance as a country yokel. We bid our King safe passage and God's good grace in his continued arduous journey, in which he would be hunted like a criminal.

With Richard as his guide and guardian, he left through a back door that led to an uncertain future for him and all those who had put their own safety at risk. At that moment I felt that the burden that had been placed on our shoulders was for a cause far greater than just the life of one man, even if that man be our King. It was for the future of our country and the freedom of all his subjects throughout this land.

We all prepared to ride on again. The Duke of Buckingham, the Earl of Derby, Earl Lauderdale and Lord Talbot, as well as several others, had decided to escape north towards Newport in Shropshire in order to re-join General Leslie and the Scots Cavalry. They persuaded me to guide them as I knew that part of the country. Still weary from the ride through the night and having had no opportunity to sleep, we set out into the half-light of dawn. The heavy, gray sky that lay before us reflected the mood in our hearts and the cold wind and rain that hindered our progress, seemed to be taunting us on our journey, as if to say that our quest would end in failure and defeat and all we had striven for these last few weeks would be lost. However, we understood how imperative our cause was, and like the shaft of light that broke through the clouds, our hearts still retained a glimmer of hope that our endeavours would one day prevail.

* * *

[The darkness in the room seemed to deepen as the tragedy of Giffard's account unfolded. Ellen could feel in her own consciousness the despair of Colonel Careless, full of anxiety for his King and frantic with worry for his son, missing after the disastrous battle. However, her spirits calmed and lifted as the next witness came forward. A tall, strong countryman, who had the appearance of having laboured many years, Richard Penderel was the embodiment of dependability.]

CHAPTER 5

Testimony of Richard Penderel of Hobbal Grange, called by the King, "Trusty Dick"

The Penderels have been ordinary, country working people in this quiet part of Staffordshire for as far back as anyone remembers. Many of us in several generations have worked for the Giffard family as farm labourers, servants or millers. My father worked for them as an under steward on their estate until the time of his death a while ago. Under the shelter of the Giffards, who harboured and hid priests, we have stayed loyal to the Old Faith, and often played our part in concealing these same priests or helping them to journey on in their missions. We know how to keep a secret; whom to trust and whom to deceive; when to confide and when to conceal. Decisions have to be made swiftly and we know all the local paths and ways, safe houses and hiding places.

My mother Joan, a strong minded, devout and determined woman, had six sons and a daughter Margaret, all loyal to the Catholic faith and to the King. My brother Thomas had gone to fight for Charles I but to our mother's grief was captured and sent overseas to Barbados to labour on the sugar plantations, where he subsequently died. John and George worked at White Ladies for the

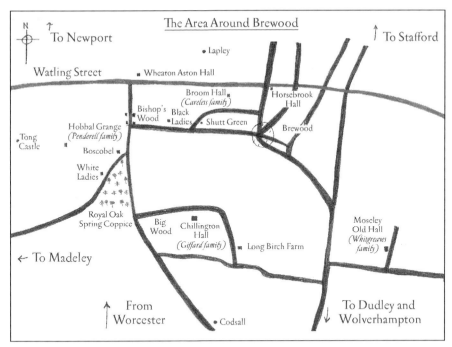

A map of the area around Brewood.

Giffards; that old house had several people living there including an old man, Mr. Walker, who was secretly a priest. The poor people in the area who were Catholic resorted to him for their devotions and Mr. John Huddleston, the priest at Moseley Old Hall, used to visit him to pray and say their Holy Office together.

My eldest brother William and his wife were servants and caretakers of Boscobel, a hunting lodge of the Giffard family. Humphrey was the tenant working the corn mill on the little stream at the back of White Ladies. I for my part lived at our family home, Hobbal Grange, a small farm belonging to the Giffards about a mile away from White Ladies, with my wife Mary, my mother Joan and my little daughter Nan. I had known William Careless and his family all my life; working with him at his farm, meeting him at secret gatherings for Mass and seeing him ride off to war. I knew he was a man you could trust with your life.

When I was awoken in the early hours to be told there were many Royalist soldiers arriving at White Ladies, my mind was immediately engaged on what measures must be taken. As I came to the house at White Ladies I was greeted by Mr Charles Giffard, exhausted from the fighting and the long ride and very agitated with the situation regarding the King. He seemed greatly relieved to see me.

"Richard!" he ordered, "Hurry back to your house and bring your best clothes for the King so he can be dressed as a countryman. Thank goodness, you are nearly as tall as he is, for there are not many around here of his height!"

I ran back to my house and returned as quickly as I could, with my jerkin and breeches of coarse cloth and a doeskin leather doublet. I had thought that my working clothes would be a better disguise than my best suit. Glad I was to meet my brother William arriving from Boscobel about the same time as I came up to the door.

We were brought quickly into the house where we met with the Earl of Derby, a sincere, pleasant gentleman whom we both remembered helping a few weeks before. He took us into an inner room and there, drinking small beer was a tall, very imposing young man. "This is the King," said Lord Derby, "Thou must have a care of him and preserve him as thou didst me."

Mr Giffard also spoke to us most earnestly to have a special care of the King and the thought overwhelmed me that among all these fine nobles and gentry and officers in the house, it was now my brothers and I who were the ones who knew best how to conceal the King and help him to escape his mortal enemies.

They had already begun to change his appearance by rubbing soot into his hands and hacking at his hair with a knife. With a hat from Humphrey, a noggin shirt from Edward Martin, and my jerkin, doublet and breeches, we transformed His Majesty into a working man. The shoes were a problem for he had long feet, but we durst not let him wear his fine leather boots. The largest shoes we could find were William Cresswell's, but we had to cut them a bit to get them on. His own clothes, a buff coat, a linen doublet and grey breeches, he gave to us brothers to hide. We hid them first in the privy, and then buried them underground for a few weeks.

I was struck with how young he appeared, only about twenty-one, and what ease of manner he had with us, though we were of such a lower class than he was. Even in such a desperate situation, he smiled and laughed at the remarkable change in his appearance, especially when Lord Wilmot cut his hair so unevenly. He was gracious enough to thank me when I was able to barber him more neatly.

William and I now urged their noble lords to make haste, for we were anxious that the house might be searched soon. We had heard that there were Parliament troops at Codsall only three miles away. Our experience told us that it would be easier to conceal a man on his own, and the danger lay in the large number of Royalists at the house. I thought it best to hide in the woods nearby, so I quietly slipped out of the back door with the King and walked with him about half a mile to Spring Coppice, while my brothers William, Humphrey and George went scouting around to see what was happening and what news they could bring to His Majesty.

So it was that at sunrise on the Thursday morning, only twenty-four hours after he had risen to engage in that dreadful battle at Worcester, and having had no sleep, King Charles walked out into the rain of a Staffordshire autumn morning, carrying a wood bill which I had put into his hand to make it appear he was a wood cutter. It seemed the heavens wept bitterly and even though I led him to the densest part of the coppice, there was not enough shelter to keep him dry, nor was there anywhere to sit. I thought I would borrow a blanket from my wife's sister, Mrs Yates, who lived nearby, so I left him by himself for a short time while I fetched it.

She was an honest, sensible woman, married to Francis Yates, and I knew she could be trusted so I explained the situation to her. She at once gave me her best blanket and offered to bring His Majesty some breakfast. The King was glad to see me come back with the blanket, which I folded and placed on the ground for him to sit on, and he was even more pleased, but a little surprised to see a woman bringing him food, a mess of eggs, butter, sugar and milk, cooked in the country style.

"Good woman," he said cheerfully, "can you be faithful to a distressed Cavalier?"

"Yes, sir I will die rather than discover you," she answered, at which the King became more serious and thanked her most sincerely. He ate the food with a pewter spoon from the black earthenware cup that she had brought it in, and liked it well, though he mistakenly guessed it was milk and apples. He was generous enough to share it with George, who like the king, had expressed that he was hungry.

My brothers reported to us that troops had come to White Ladies enquiring if the King and his horsemen had passed that way. Some people from the village had told them that a party of horsemen had come that way three hours ago but had moved on. The troops had asked which way they had gone and had set off in eager pursuit.

I stayed with the King all day in the wood, George and William coming and going with news. John had been given charge of Lord Wilmot and had led him off to find somewhere to hide elsewhere. We spent the time teaching the King to be a country fellow, showing him how to walk less tall and straight but instead with a rolling, lopsided gait, and we taught him the speech of common local people. He was quick to learn, partly because he had talked with many Staffordshire soldiers in the weeks before Worcester and as well as this I think he had a natural gift for acting.

He talked a great deal of what route he should take to escape; London, Scotland or Wales were all possibilities, but I told him I did not know any safe houses on the way to London. Eventually, he

decided to try for Wales, and I said I would guide him to the River
Severn and once in Wales he might be able to head for Swansea, or
some other port that traded with France. We would have to journey
by night for safety, so I proposed that we go back to my house about
five o'clock to eat before we set out.

My wife was used to me bringing a brother or a fellow worker
home for a meal unexpectedly, but I think she was awestruck when I
came in with the King, as well as Humphrey, George and Francis
Yates. However, good housewife that she is, and filled with motherly
concern at the weary state of him, she quickly busied herself with
preparing a hearty meal of eggs and bacon for us all. While we were
waiting and he was sitting in my good chair, my little daughter Nan
came up to him, looking curiously at this tall stranger. He took a
liking to her and sat her on his knee and talked kindly to her,
sometimes making her laugh with merry jokes, sometimes talking
sadly about the great fight he had seen at Worcester.

In a few minutes my wife gave him a large plateful of food, and
after he had eaten a little he asked me to have some as well. "Yes, sir
I will" I said and he teased me. "You have a better stomach than I,
for you have eaten five times today already." In truth he had eaten as
often as I had that day, for he had a young man's appetite, but I was
not minded to dispute with a King!

We discussed the best way of journeying to Wales, and the King
suggested we wait until dusk. While we were talking, my mother
Joan came in, eager to see him. I felt proud of her, seeing her afresh
through the King's eyes, a strong indomitable woman, used to ruling
over six wilful sons, in widowhood having to strive against hardship,
in recusancy having to be determined in believing what she did was
right. She had qualities the King would also need if he were ever to
attain his throne.

She spoke to him sincerely, and with the authority we Penderel
brothers knew so well.

"I thank God my sons are honoured to be the means of delivering you safely, your Majesty. I bless you and pray earnestly for you to come through these dangerous times and one day to rule as our most beloved King."

He was most touched by her warm words and said he would always remember her and her sons.

My brother-in-law Francis Yates then expressed concern that King Charles would need money for his venture. He had been sent by the King to Mr Giffard to borrow money to supply his needs but had missed him and come back empty handed. He offered him thirty shillings in silver from his own money. I think His Majesty realized that this was a large sum for a working man and would only accept ten. Everyone was eager to help. Humphrey wanted to go ahead and see if anyone was about but the King would not let him, thinking he should not let any more be in danger than necessary. As it grew dark and time to go, the others took leave of the King, kneeling down before him and beseeching God to guide him and bless him.

The King and I set off towards the River Severn. I intended to cross at a ferry that I knew of halfway between Shrewsbury and Bridgnorth. It would be a walk of about ten miles across dark countryside but the King was in good spirits for it. His youthfulness gave him a sense of adventure. About midnight we came to a mill and we could hear some men talking. I whispered to the King that if they questioned us, he should not answer, because his voice would show he was not a country man.

We had to pass the mill to keep on the road to the river, and as we came near the door I could see the miller in his white clothes, sitting in his doorway. He called out warily,

"Who goes there?" so I answered,

"Neighbours going home!"

"If you be neighbours, stand, or I'll knock you down!"

I thought there might be men in the house and we had best get away, so I bade the King, "Follow me closely Sir!" and opening a gate into a narrow path began to run. The miller began to shout loudly,

"Rogues! Rogues!" and men came running out of the house. My instinct had been right for they seemed like soldiers. We ran up the dirty lane for as long as our legs would run, but it was deep in mud. When we could run no more I told him to leap over the hedge and we lay still to see if anyone was following. For about an hour we kept quiet in the moonless blackness, then hearing no more noise we went on to try to reach Madeley, in order to cross the Severn there.

I was hoping to seek help there from a Catholic gentleman I had had dealings with before, Mr Woolf, whose house had some priests' hiding holes. But the King told me to go ahead alone to ask first if Mr Woolf was prepared to risk hiding such a dangerous person. He stayed hiding under a great tree by a hedge, while I went into the house.

I asked Mr. Woolf if he could hide an English gentleman for a day until we could get across the River the next night, but he was in a nervous state, the town being full of soldiers.

"I will not risk my neck for anyone, except it be the King himself!" he declared. Then, because I had had dealings with the man before, and trusting that I understood his character, I told him urgently that it was indeed the King, in desperate need of help. At that, he replied stoutly that he would risk everything he had in the world to protect His Majesty. Hurrying back to the King I told him everything that had been said, but he was troubled that I had been indiscreet. I assured him that the man was trustworthy, and as it was growing light, he was persuaded to come into the house or face greater danger.

Old Mr. Woolf greeted the King anxiously. "I am sorry to see you here, Your Majesty, for the town has two companies of militia keeping guard on the ferry, questioning everyone who passes, and my hiding places are of no use now because they were discovered last time they searched my house. If any soldiers came here it would be the first place they would look. The only thing to be done is for you to hide in my barn behind the hay."

To this we had to agree, and we made our way to the barn, carrying some cold meat which he gave us, and glad of it we were after a night of walking. The two of us lay there all that drizzly September day, sometimes talking, sometimes dozing, but it was not easy to sleep long for we were alert to every sound of people coming or going. Near evening, there was some commotion as Mr. Woolf's son, who had been held prisoner at Shrewsbury, arrived home, much to the relief of the old gentleman. When it was dark they came into the barn to share some more meat with us and the four of us discussed what to do. Mr. Woolf's son advised us not to try to go to Wales, for he had seen dozens of guards posted all along the Severn to prevent fugitives from Worcester escaping that way. Reluctantly the King decided to return to my house and try to make contact with Lord Wilmot, with the view of escaping with that gentleman to London.

The way back was difficult and depressing. The previous night we had set out in brave spirits, believing we would make progress with delivering him; now we felt set back and disappointed, all our efforts wasted. The lanes seemed even dirtier than before, full of holes and ruts, added to which we were tired from walking so far. One time the King, his shoes full of mud and stones, sat down and did not want to stir, for his feet were exceedingly sore. This was the one occasion when I saw him express despair, so I persuaded, cajoled and encouraged him, saying the way ahead might be easier or we had not far to go, until his spirits rose, he forced himself up and continued walking. Later it was his turn to give me courage. Not wanting to risk disturbing the owner of the mill again, the King suggested we should turn aside and cross the river.

"No, sir," I objected, "It is a scurvy river, not easy to cross and I cannot swim."

"It is only a small stream. I will help you Richard," he replied, and so it was that I, a lowly Staffordshire country labourer, found myself up to my waist in water, in the midnight darkness, being helped across the river by the hand of my Sovereign King.

At long last, about three in the morning, we came back to near White Ladies, but rather than stay at the same place again, which I feared the soldiers might be watching, I thought to bring him to where my brother William lived, a hunting lodge of Sir Giffard, secluded in the woods, with a secret hiding place. This house bore the name of Boscobel.

Fearing that soldiers might be there, I told the King to stay hidden in the woods while I went to see if the house were safe. To my great surprise and joy, who should I find there but Colonel Careless, who I thought was missing or dead at Worcester? He had thought that if he went to his own home at Broom Hall, he might bring danger to his family, so he, like me, had decided to ask William for help.

I explained to them both that the King was in the woods and they came with me to meet him. We found His Majesty sitting on a tree root, and we brought him into the shelter of the house. William's wife Joan, as my own Mary had been, was shocked at his exhausted state and busied herself quickly to bring him some bread and cheese, with a posset of thin milk and small beer, all of which he ate and drank eagerly. She also warmed up some water to bathe his feet, which he complained were much blistered from the ill-fitting shoes. Colonel Careless himself knelt down and pulled off the King's shoes, which were full of mud and gravel and the stockings which were soaking wet. He gently bathed the King's feet while William's wife brought some hot embers to place in the shoes to dry them.

Although the King then wanted to rest and find a bed in the house, Colonel Careless advised that it would be safer to hide in the woods. He undertook to keep watch over the King, for he could see how weary I was.

"Go home and rest, Richard, see your wife and catch up with your neglected work. I promise I will guard His Majesty with my life," he assured me.

Richard Penderel.

I felt a great weight lifting from my shoulders. It put me in mind of one time when I had gathered a great load of wood, but evening was coming on and I was struggling to carry it. Unexpectedly by chance, my brother John met me in the lane and smiling, took half the weight from me, and helped me to bear it home. The responsibility that I had borne for two days for the King's safety was now being taken by my old, loyal friend William Careless.

* * *

[Ellen smiled as Richard Penderel stepped back, nodding his head respectfully to the next witness, a personage of splendid height. Thoughts and impressions were whirling round her mind as His Majesty King Charles II took the centre of the room. With his long, dark face, his wide generous mouth and laughing yet watchful eyes, behind which a hidden melancholy could sometimes be seen, he had a presence which centred all attention on him and inspired all who beheld him with awe and admiration. He spoke in a cultured accent with a lively tone, as though relating a reminiscence he had often enjoyed repeating.]

CHAPTER 6

Testimony of His Majesty King Charles II, by the Grace of God Sovereign of England, Scotland, Wales and Ireland

Colonel Careless greeting King Charles in Boscobel Woods, with Richard Penderel nearby.

My body and soul were at their lowest ebb as I sat there under a tree waiting for Dick Penderel to return. Two nights of traipsing through rough countryside, with danger at every turn, had left me weary to the bone. It can be imagined therefore, with what relief I beheld Penderel coming towards me with Colonel Careless at his side.

This was a man whom I knew to be one of my most loyal and experienced soldiers, added to which I had thought he was killed or captured at Worcester. They brought me into the house, where we breakfasted, and Careless bathed my poor feet with warm water, which I much appreciated.

I was looking forward to a sleep in a bed, but the Colonel insisted it was too dangerous to stay in the house that day. "Even the woods are not safe, Your Majesty," warned Careless. "The soldiers will be searching everywhere. The only thing we can do, is what I have done before, find a large, thick branched tree in which to hide."

Yielding to the Colonel's experience, I let myself be guided into a dense part of the wood, where Careless chose a large oak tree that had been pollarded three or four years ago, so that the branches had grown out again very thick and leafy. William Penderel had brought a ladder, which Careless and I used to climb high into the tree, and the good wife Joan handed us up bread, and cheese wrapped in a clean cloth, and a pillow for me to be more comfortable. Seeing that I was very tired after three nights of travelling, the Colonel told me to lay my limbs on the pillow and rest my head in his lap, so that I could sleep.

The poor fellow must have been most uncomfortable and stiff, sitting on the hard branches, not daring to move for hours. He admitted later that his arm which was supporting me had become completely numb. What thoughts must have been going through his mind, situated there, high in a tree, with the King of England sleeping in his sole care. I slept awhile, but awoke to find the Colonel gently pinching me, to warn me that soldiers were nearby. Peering

Colonel Careless helping King Charles into the oak tree.

down through the leaves, I could see the men going up and down searching all through the woods. It was a tense moment. I felt the fear tightening my chest and my pulse beating hard. However, the attention of the soldiers was somewhat diverted by Joan Penderel, William's wife, going up and down among the trees, making a distraction by gathering sticks. After a while the troops moved away back to the lane, riding away elsewhere, and we could breathe again.

Feeling safer now, the Colonel unwrapped the bread and cheese and we ate it hungrily, washed down with the small beer that these country people provided so often. Many banquets I have partaken of, before and since, which I did not enjoy as much as that simple fare, being ravenously hungry. All the while, William and Joan kept walking round and about the woods, pretending to work but keeping watch on my behalf. Later in the afternoon, Joan handed up more food for us, with a long nut-hook.

At times, when we were sure there was no-one nearby, we were able to talk about what had happened at Worcester after I had left. He had continued fighting till the very end and saw the last man killed in that battle. I was grieved to hear how many good men were slain or taken prisoner, including the Duke of Hamilton, who had been shot in the leg and taken captive into the Commandery; Careless had heard that he was very ill and likely to die there of his wound.

Colonel Careless was older than I was, about forty years of age, and had spent many years of his life fighting in the Royalist Cause, first for my father and now for me. He had sacrificed much in terms of his family, his wealth and his freedom. Shorter than me (but then most men are) sturdy, strong, having a round, plain, honest countenance with an expression of openness, he gave to me a sense of confidence and trust. Many noble men I have kept company with, but few inspired me with such trustworthiness. Many higher-ranking generals I have fought alongside, who may have appeared more distinguished, but Careless was as capable as any.

When I asked him whether he knew what had happened to his son, his eyes clouded with an expression of pain and worry. "I searched for him for hours, but in vain. Not having found him among the dead, I hoped that he had escaped, but I know not whether he rode for London, Wales or Scotland. I decided to head for home, thinking he might have done the same. Passing by Hartlebury Castle I had some difficulty, for an enemy garrison was there but I managed to break through and come by secret, hidden roads to Staffordshire. One night I came across Tong Heath, and was sheltered by a man I know there, David Jones for two days. Another friend then helped me; a lady called Elizabeth Burgess accompanied me so that I should not be so conspicuous and brought me to my home, Broom Hall, to let my brother John and my poor dear wife know that I am safe."

"They were relieved to see me, but no-one around has seen or heard of my son William, and my wife is frantic with anxiety for him. I could not endanger them by staying there, so I came over here, thinking I would hide at Boscobel, then journey on, to make my escape to the Continent."

We discussed all means of which way I myself should go, and I wondered if I should stay with the Colonel, who was so wise, resourceful, and experienced in this kind of situation. But at last I decided to try to meet up again as agreed, with Lord Wilmot, who according to one of the Penderel brothers, was still hiding in the area.

As it drew towards evening, we thought it safe to come down out of the tree and go back into the house. We were both glad to move our aching, weary limbs, for it was impossible to be comfortable on the hard branches. It was a smallish, plain house, built as a hunting lodge in the woods by John Giffard some twenty years before, and they showed me a hiding place where they proposed I should spend the night. It was small and cramped but I liked it much better than the prospect of sitting in the tree again.

While we were sitting talking Humphrey Penderel, the miller, came in and was relating how he had gone into Shifnal during the day, on the excuse of paying some tax money to Captain Broadway of the Parliamentary troops there, but in reality, to pick up any news or rumours going about. While he was there, in came a Parliamentary colonel fresh from Worcester, who was in pursuit of the King. He had been told that I had been at White Ladies, and he began to question Humphrey closely, reminding him that to help the King could be punishable by death and that a thousand pound reward was being offered for information. The quick-witted Penderel told him that he believed a group of Cavaliers had been at White Ladies the day after the battle and the King may have been among them, but they had moved on and he did not know where any of them were now. Humphrey and his brothers were pleased with the way he had seemed to answer with candour, while concealing the most important facts, but I was dismayed to realize the extent of the danger I was putting the brothers into, and how tempting it must be to have the chance of a lifetime's wages if they chose to betray me.

Humphrey saw the look on my face, and faltered in his tale, embarrassed, but Colonel Careless, tactfully put right the situation.

"Your Majesty," he intervened, "if it were one hundred thousand pounds, it were to no purpose, and I engage my soul for the true characters of this family."

I felt reassured by this, and soon we sat down merrily to a supper of chicken which Mistress Joan had cooked for us. We were laughing and exchanging jests about the way William, thinking Richard's barbering not neat enough, had cut my hair yet again, short on the top but longer about the ears, in the country style of those parts.

Having finished, Mistress Joan asked me what I would like to eat the next day, and I, not considering, said I would fancy some mutton. Only later did I become aware that, as they were not well off, it was unusual for them to eat meat such as that, except on special occasions, the last being the christening of their child. If they were to go buying expensive meat it would arouse suspicions. They did not tell me this at the time, but Colonel Careless, understanding their difficulty, undertook to solve it by going out in the dark to a neighbour's field and killing one of his sheep with a dagger. He and William Penderel carried it back to the house to cook it. Being an honest man, he later admitted to the neighbour, a Mr. William Staunton, what he had done, and offered to pay for it, but Staunton when he heard that the sheep was for my dinner, refused payment. This was yet another example of the generosity of these people.

That night was exceedingly uncomfortable again, cramped into the hole beneath the attic floor, hardly big enough for a man of my height to lie straight. They had given me a pillow to lie down on, but even so, I was up early, glad to be out of that place. My mind dwelt on who else might have sheltered there, maybe priests in terror of their lives merely for practising their beliefs. All the time the Penderel brothers were looking out, walking constantly outside the house in case anyone should come up the road.

This was Sunday, and as the woods had been searched the day before, and as many of the soldiers, being Puritans, were likely to be at their prayers, we thought it safe to be in the house that day. I spent the morning walking up and down the gallery, sometimes looking out of the window towards the road for soldiers, and other times praying and reading, as befitted the Sabbath. In truth, of all the people in England that day, I was probably most in need of my Saviour's help and guidance. My heart was sore grieved for those hundreds of poor soldiers dead, wounded or captured in my cause, and I knew not what the future would bring.

I was called from my sad reverie to come down for lunch. I had requested that I should fry the mutton once the sheep had been cooked. They prepared a blazing fire and brought me in a frying pan, a leg of the meat, a knife and a trencher. I cut the mutton into collops and pricked them, then fried them in some butter. Colonel Careless acted as my under cook while I tended the chops, and a merry time we had of it. I had learned to cook during the years I had spent campaigning with my father through many battles, often camping out in the open, and if there was a lighter side to war, it was this experience I enjoyed, of being one of the ordinary people and sharing in the lives of my most lowly subjects.

During the afternoon, Careless, feeling that the most immediate danger of the house being searched was over, undertook to keep watch while I spent a time of peace and quiet in the garden.

There was a quaint little arbour on a mound near the house and I found it most pleasant to sit reading there, the first time I had felt at ease for many days.

Later, another of the brothers, John, who had been put in charge of helping Lord Wilmot to hide in safety, arrived and told me that Lord Wilmot was at the home of Mr. Whitgreave, nearby at Moseley. I sent John back with a message that I would join Lord Wilmot at Moseley that night, for I had decided to try to get away from that area with my old friend.

We had some trouble finding a horse for me to travel on; my feet were still so sore that I did not wish to walk five miles on the rough paths through the woods. Colonel Careless, ever resourceful, remembered that Humphrey Penderel the miller had a horse, and he was called on to lend it for my use. About eleven o'clock that night the horse, with an ancient saddle on it, was brought up to the gate at Boscobel. I expressed the wish that only Colonel Careless and John Penderel should come with me, but the brothers protested that it was dangerous for just the three of us to venture out and they insisted that they should all accompany me. At this, Careless told me humbly that he should take his leave of me. He felt that as he was so well known about that part of the country, his presence would raise suspicions. It was a wrench for me to part from him, for I had grown to have a deep regard for this honest, dependable, utterly trustworthy veteran soldier.

"What will you do and where will you go?" I asked him. "You have risked everything, even your life and your family to serve me, as you did for my father."

"I will make my way abroad, Your Majesty, as I have before, perhaps to France or most likely to Holland. And maybe, if it pleases Almighty God, I will return when you return to take up your rightful Kingdom."

"If I ever do gain my throne, it will be thanks to such loyal subjects as you, and I promise you Careless, I will never forget you, nor cease to be grateful to you. Indeed, Careless seems not the right name for you, for you have taken great care of me these two days! I would give you the name Carlos, for that is my name Charles in Spanish, and then you and your family would always be known for your great heroism in preserving me."

Having spoken these words, I grasped Careless's hand in a firm, fervent handshake. With some difficulty I mounted the bony, old horse, and set off through the dark woods with Richard, William, Humphrey, John, and George Penderel, as well as their brother-in-law Francis Yates, surrounding me like a strange, royal retinue. I glanced back once to see the trusted companion, who had given strength to my spirits by his presence, standing stock still with his hand raised in a farewell salute, until I should be gone safely from his sight.

Although I was grateful not to have to walk, the old farm horse was slow and clumsy, compared to the fine horses that I was accustomed to, and I complained jestingly that it was "the heaviest dull jade I ever rode on," to which Humphrey, ever ready with a quick answer, replied,

"My Liege, can you blame the horse to go heavily when he has the weight of three kingdoms on his back?" the which answer pleased me mightily, not only for its wit but also the respect and honour it showed for my status. In this manner we travelled on to Moseley, and after that, with the help of the excellent Jane Lane of Bentley Hall, and in the company of my reckless friend Wilmot, I made my way, with many adventures, across England to France; thereafter it was some while before I met with the good Colonel again, when we were both in exile.

* * *

An Oake was thought most safe, from what could prove,

More luckie than the sacred tree to Jove.

See where the Hen-roost Ladder stands by that,

The Mighty Monarch climb'd the Boughs of State

Where Noble Carlos lent his manlike Knee

The last support of fainting Majestie.

(A verse from a contemporary ballad)

The Whitgreaves parlour at Moseley Old Hall.

[King Charles doffed his wide-brimmed hat and bowed elegantly to Ellen as he finished his account. She was overwhelmed by the glamour and majesty of his presence but her mood changed as she became aware of the next witness, a priest, who struggled to walk across the room. Though he was not old, he was stooped and worn down, appearing to be weary beyond endurance. Some wasting illness was clearly sapping the life from him. In a chivalrous gesture, the King took the invalid's arm to support him and brought him safely to a chair. It took him a moment to gather the breath to speak, in a low, hoarse voice.]

CHAPTER 7

Testimony of William Careless (the younger), son of Colonel William Careless

I am the son of Colonel William Careless (he brought each word out with a great effort.) Near the end of my life I wrote this statement to record how much my father meant to me and how I lived my life according to the ideals with which he raised me. (Unrolling a parchment, the frail man began to read to Ellen.)

The Statement of William Careless the younger, son of Colonel William Careless at the English College of Rome *(This account is recorded in the scholars' interrogatories, kept in the English College in Rome.)*

My name is William Carlos, alias Dorrington, the eldest son of my father, of the same name. I was born in the town of Brewood, Staffordshire, where I was brought up till my twelfth year. The civil war having broken out, I spent my thirteenth and fourteenth years in Tonge Castle, of which my father was the governor. My father being taken prisoner and sent into banishment, my mother returned to Brewood, where I lived until I had completed my eighteenth year; at which time my father secretly returning to London from Spain, but not being allowed to live in England, escaped into Lower Germany and took me with him as companion, where I spent my nineteenth year, and in my twentieth year we joined the Scottish army of King Charles II at Worcester, and being there separated from my father in the battle, I journeyed towards London and remained there until this my twenty-fourth year.

My parents were of the middle class but reduced to the lowest condition by the war. I have an only brother who lives with my parents, who are Catholics.

I made my humanity studies at Brewood and Tongue, and was always a Catholic, and left London on the 4th July, 1655. On witnessing the execution of the most blessed martyr, Mr. Southworth, I resolved to seek Rome, in order, as far as in me lies, to render some service, however unworthy, to Holy Church.

It is my sole desire to embrace the ecclesiastical state.

(Signed William Carlos)

When I read those words again, after so many years, the ardour and the idealism that I felt at that time lives in me again. Two heroes inspired me in my life; my father who encouraged me to be a soldier and John Southworth who enthused me to be a priest. Now, looking back over my life, enduring what I feel will be my last illness, I am still grateful to those two men, each remarkable in his own way. I never achieved the heroic deeds of my father in warfare nor did I reach the heights of holiness of blessed Southworth. Not for me is the honour of bravery in battle, nor the brief, transitory agony, followed by eternal glory, of martyrdom.

It was very hard for my mother and for me when my father was taken prisoner to Stafford, then was forced to go into exile across the sea. She occupied herself with caring for my younger brother Thomas while I continued my studies. When my father came back and encouraged me to go to Lower Germany with him, to learn to be a soldier, she was heart-broken to part from me, but I was eager to go adventuring with him. It was not in her generous nature to stand in the way of our quest for championing the King's cause and thus I was allowed to go abroad with my father, and then when we returned to England to join the King's Scots' army, again she was anxious but wished us God's blessing as we set out for that fateful convergence at Worcester.

During that dreadful day I lost sight of my father; neither of us knew what had happened to the other. Someone told me later that my father had with much difficulty escaped thither from Worcester, where he had stayed to see the last man die, being a man of that valour that durst not leave a field as long as there remained a friend to be assisted or an enemy to be subdued.

Parted from my father in the turmoil of battle, the only way I found clear was the road to London, swept along with several other fellow soldiers fleeing from the rout which had become a massacre. In the Capital, though it was dangerous, I found places to live secretly, especially among fellow Catholics who were used to hiding and sheltering those sought by the authorities. Thus I came into contact with the priest John Southworth.

At that time, he was working as he had for many years among the poorest people in the dreadful slums of London. Undeterred by deadly diseases or filthy conditions, he brought the Sacraments to all who asked for them, giving Communion to those who were ill and hearing the confessions of the dying as well as anointing them. Many had fallen away from their Faith through fear of the law or lack of opportunity, there being few priests; but in the face of death they wished to be reconciled and to receive Extreme Unction according to the tradition of their ancestors. John Southworth was always willing to minister to them, risking his life in every hovel that he entered.

Originally from Lancashire, he had grown up in a time of great persecution at the end of Queen Elizabeth's reign, and had gone to Douay in Belgium to train as a priest. Although he knew it was treason to be a Catholic priest in England, he came back here after being ordained in 1619; at the age of twenty-seven he began a life of service and dangerous risks. Arrested in 1625 at Lancaster, he was imprisoned in the castle there with a Jesuit priest, Edmund Arrowsmith and a Benedictine, Edward Barlow. It was said that when Edmund Arrowsmith was led out through the castle courtyard to his execution, he looked up to the window where John Southworth was prisoner and saw him looking down, ready to bless and absolve his friend. The condemned prisoner, on the way to the hurdle, lifted up his hands and received his absolution from his fellow priest with great joy and humility. Some said it seemed a light shone down from the prison window to the gallows.

Because King Charles I had married the French Catholic Henrietta Maria, there was some easing of the persecution of Catholics. Mr. Southworth was reprieved, and at the request of Queen Henrietta Maria, along with fifteen other priests, was put in the care of the French Ambassador, to be sent in exile abroad. It seemed he soon returned to London, if he ever left, for he was soon imprisoned again in the Clink at Southwark.

This was the start of over twenty years of his living in and out of prison in London. Whenever he was incarcerated, he said Mass for his fellow prisoners. Sometimes he was allowed out on parole, and this was when he set up a heroic ministry to the poor, sick and dying, risking his life with every visit, by betrayal or from catching the deadly diseases.

I met him on a few occasions, for some of my fellow Catholics who were sheltering me in London, invited me to join them at Mass. We would tread warily up old staircases into shadowy, hidden attics. John Southworth would enter the dimly lit room with head bowed and begin the Mass, speaking low and reverently. His face was worn and gaunt from years of hardship, but still infused with passion for his priestly calling and lit with love for his Saviour whom he served. How consoling it was for me to hear again those familiar Latin phrases, so well known to me from my youngest days. "In nomine Patris et Filii et Spiritus Sancti" as we gathered to worship, "Sanctus, Sanctus, Sanctus," as we praised God, and "Domine, non sum dignus" as we prepared to receive the Holy Communion. In my mind I was back once more to the times when, seated securely between my parents, I had attended secret Masses at Chillington or Moseley Hall, in similar ancient, dusty, garrets.

The dangers of meeting for Mass were much greater in London at this time than it had been back in Staffordshire in those former years. Now the King had been removed, the Catholic Queen was exiled in France and the Puritans were at the height of their powers. The inevitable news came to us, in June 1654 that Southworth had been arrested from his lodgings in Westminster, where the sacred vessels that he used for Mass were found in his room. He would not deny what he used them for. He had been betrayed by a pursuivant named Jefferies, one of those treacherous undesirables who earn money by hunting for priests then demand bribes to keep secret. Colonel Worsley who arrested Mr. Southworth was unfortunately one of Cromwell's most zealously puritanical officers.

The trial was most moving, the magistrate himself being in tears as with difficulty, hardly able to speak, he pronounced the sentence. The judges tried to save John Southworth's life, asking him to plead not guilty to the charge of being a priest ordained by the authority of the See of Rome and resident within the Commonwealth of

England. But Southworth would not deny that he was a priest, for he took it that it would be denying his religion. When the death sentence was pronounced, he fell on his knees and said,

> "O Lord God, I humbly thank thee, who hath made me worthy to suffer for Thy sake."

Terrible as it was to attend his execution, some of the Catholic community who had been served by him, thought that we should go in order to console him and strengthen him by our presence. On the 28th June, thousands of people gathered at Tyburn Gallows to witness the event, some in coaches, some with ghoulish curiosity and several with sympathy for a good man unjustly condemned. Nine men and one woman were to be put to death, five of them forgers of coins. Thus it was that like our Saviour, John was executed among criminals. Because he was a priest, he was kept until last, and allowed to address the crowd.

He was already suffering, having being dragged on a hurdle from Newgate prison, but clothed in his priest's gown and a four-cornered hat, he spoke in a controlled yet passionate manner. He told us that he had not wished to act against the secular government, merely to teach Christ's faith, handed down to us through the Apostles. He never acted against the Protector, Oliver Cromwell, but only wanted to save men's souls. In following Christ, he was willing to imitate His Holy death. At this point he gazed up at the scaffold and said,

> "This gallows I look on as His Cross, which I gladly take to follow my dear Saviour."

It was when he uttered the words, "I plead not for myself (I came hither to suffer) but for you poor persecuted Catholics whom I leave

Saint John Southworth.

behind me", that his gaze met mine for a moment, with a look of such intensity that I felt he was communicating some word of command to me. I understood in that split second that I was called to continue his work. The words of Jesus that he had quoted were burned into my heart, "He that will be My disciple, let him take up his cross and follow Me."

I too, was called to serve the Lord as a priest. Like a servant bearing a flickering candle through a dark place, I would carry forward the precious Faith preserved by our fathers, now handed on to me from the blessed John Southworth. It might be another hundred years or so, but the Catholic Faith would survive and eventually flourish, in our beloved country.

I cannot bear to describe the dreadful way that he was tortured as he died. I could not help but turn my head away. How human beings could inflict such butchery on any man, let alone one of such goodness and piety, I cannot understand. I can only aver that I was not deterred from my purpose; on the contrary my resolve was strengthened by Southworth's unfailing courage, determination and constancy.

I applied as soon as I could to the English College of Rome, and on the 9th of September the next year, 1655, I entered as an alumnus, I chose to train to be a Jesuit, for having been a soldier before deciding to be a priest, I felt that I was following the example of Ignatius Loyola, who had founded the Society of Jesus. After a year in Rome, I was sent to join the novitiate of the Society at Messina in Sicily on the 6th of May 1656.

The greatest difficulty I experienced was informing my mother and my father of the path that I was choosing to take. Communication was uncertain, for letters took so long to be delivered, and in my father's case, I did not know where he was for many months. Both parents I know, were glad that I should follow such a noble calling and serve God. However, mixed with such sentiments was great fearfulness for the dangers I would face if I should ever come back to England.

There followed for me the happiest, most satisfying years of my life, studying and living with like-minded men of holy purpose. There was an overwhelming sense of freedom, living in countries where I was completely free to live and worship as a Roman Catholic.

The training of a Jesuit takes many years, longer than ordinary secular priests, but my mind responded eagerly to all the studying and learning.

The only sadness that I had was to be so far away from my family. How my father fared in those years, I knew little, except for rare letters delivered months after they had been written. Much of what happened I learnt of in later times, when we were both back in England, after the death of Cromwell and the blessed restoration of our beloved Monarch.

Returning to the period when he was at Boscobel; after the King had left for Moseley with the Penderel brothers, my father sought help from a friend of his, Humphrey Ironmonger of neighbouring Wolverhampton. This worthy man helped him with a pass and some money, and so he was able to travel to the Continent where he was the first man to give news to Charles' sister Mary, Princess of Orange, of her brother's escape.

He was always a soldier by occupation and inclination, and in 1656 he was promoted by King Charles to Colonel in the King's Royal Regiment of Guards. Lord Wentworth, who had fought many battles on the Royalist side during the Civil War, was given the responsibility to organize and command this regiment of foot guards, who served as a bodyguard unit to the King.

In the complicated politics of France, Spain, and the Netherlands, by 1658, the French had allied with Cromwell's Commonwealth army against Spain; King Charles, after some years of wearisome treatment from the French court, being often in a state of poverty, had made an alliance with Spain. With money granted to him from the Spanish, he hoped to build up a Royalist army to invade England once more.

On the 14th day of June that year the French forces, under their famous and brilliant commander the Vicomte de Turenne, attacked the Spanish and Royalist allies, near Dunkirk. King Charles' brother

James, Duke of York, personally led two regiments into action. My father's regiment was the last to give in when Turenne's French and Commonwealth forces were winning, just as at Worcester he had been the last Royalist soldier to leave the city. His force of the Royal Regiment of Guards only surrendered after assurances that they would be allowed to rejoin King Charles at Ypres and not be handed over to the English Commonwealth Army. My father was taken prisoner but was soon released on a half ransom.

His Majesty King Charles held my father in great regard, and in 1658 at Brussels he granted him a coat of arms by Letters Patent under the Great Seal and gave him the name Carlos, honouring him with the Spanish version of his own name. This coat of arms was very much treasured by my family. It showed an oak tree and three royal crowns; underneath the Latin motto meant, "A subject faithful to the king and the safety of the kingdom", very fitting for my father's loyalty and his life's actions.

After two more years of tedious exile, everything changed when Oliver Cromwell died, and his son Richard failed to be accepted as ruler. The English, weary of the Puritans' harsh government (when they had even tried to ban Christmas as well as candles, crucifixes, dances and sports) invited Charles to return and take up his Sovereignty. My father came back with him as Londoners poured out into the streets to welcome the King, on 29th May, his thirtieth birthday. In faraway Sicily I heard the news from England and rejoiced to think of my father being honoured and rewarded after all his years of striving and hardship. It brought joy and relief also to my mother to be reunited with him after so many lonely years during his exile.

King Charles did not forget those who had helped and sheltered him and risked their lives for him when he was a desperate fugitive. My father was granted the proceeds of the tax on hay and straw being brought into the Capital and the right to sell ballast on the River

Thames. From this time forth he was a wealthy man owning houses in Stafford and a property at Green Street at Hallow near Worcester. Much of his time was spent in London, attending to his businesses and often at the Court, for the King valued his company and friendship. No doubt the two of them often reminisced and laughed together about their time spent sitting on hard branches in the oak tree or cooking stolen mutton over the hearth fire.

He bears upon an Oake proper in a Feild Or a Fesse Gules, charged with 3 Regal Crowns of y second by the name of Carlos. And for his Creaft a Civic Crown or Oaken Garland with a Sword and Scepter crossed through it Saltierwise.

Page 86   Boorvek Dont

The coat of arms granted to William Carlos, (formerly Careless).

I was glad to hear also that our good friends the Penderels were generously remembered. The month after his triumphant arrival in London, the brothers went to Whitehall where his Majesty acknowledged their faithful service and paid them a princely reward. The next year, in 1661 they were given £400 each, but later William received more. When Richard died, the King settled an annuity on his widow Mary of £100 for her lifetime and for her heirs after her death. William and his heirs received the same. John, Humphrey and George and their descendants were granted smaller annuities. This brave, generous family were now able to live in comparative ease with a good income.

Their kinswoman Elizabeth Yates had suffered the loss of her husband Francis, when he was hanged for his part in guiding Mr. Charles Giffard, the King and others in the royal party to White Ladies. She was granted an annuity of £50 for herself and her heirs. It was good to know that these simple, working people, who had looked after the King so kindly, risking their lives for him, were now able to live in comfort.

Mr Charles Giffard, after the King had left White Ladies, had led the rest of the royal party to Newport but was captured soon after. He managed to escape and sail to Holland. Venturing back to England in 1657 he was kept prisoner at Shrewsbury Castle and ordered to stand trial, but thankfully survived it. The King gave him a life pension of £150, from 1668 but he was not very adept at managing his investments and ended up at times in prison for debt. However, he somehow managed to support his stepson, Daniel Coulster, a fellow Jesuit of mine, at the College of St. Omer in North France, for seven years.

Mr Peter Giffard had suffered much during the Civil War, having had his house Chillington Hall besieged, taken and ransacked by Parliamentary forces. His estate was sold to three men and he was forced to buy it back at nearly twelve thousand pounds, as well as enduring being imprisoned several times. He petitioned King Charles and in 1662 was granted all the money arising from the sale of his property.

Another Staffordshire Catholic gentleman who had aided the King was Thomas Whitgreave, who had welcomed him to Moseley

Hall after he had left Boscobel, guided by the five Penderel brothers. Mr. Whitgreave's mother had prepared dinner for His Majesty and given him raisins, almonds and sweetmeats when he was leaving, kneeling down to pray for him with her son and the priest, Father Huddleston. The reward for the Whitgreaves family was somewhat delayed but eventually a life pension of £300 was granted in 1666.

During his stay at Moseley, the King was much impressed with the priest, John Huddleston, who bathed his sore feet, gave up his bed for him to sleep on, kept watch for enemies, and gave him a new, clean shirt. They talked of the Catholic religion, and the King had asked to see the oratory in their house, saying "he knew Huddleston was a priest, and he need not fear to own it to him, for if it pleased God to restore him to his Kingdom, we should never need more privacies."

King Charles did indeed remember and reward Father Huddleston well, for he invited him to come to London and live at Somerset House under the protection of the King's mother, Queen Henrietta. When she died Mr. Huddleston became chaplain to the Catholic Queen Catherine of Braganza, with a salary of £100.

However, the Restoration of the King, for which we had strived during so many years, made sacrifices for, endured harsh imprisonment and exile for, even given lives for, was a disappointment to the hopes of Catholics that from henceforth we would practise our religion in freedom and safety throughout the land. Although King Charles had many sympathies for our Faith, and indeed I think he secretly would have liked to become a Catholic, he would not, as a shrewd monarch, risk disagreement or unrest from Parliament and the country.

Religion had to be settled in England to secure peace and unity in the most pragmatic way, and therefore soon after his accession, an Act of Parliament was passed preventing those not conforming to the Anglican Church from holding civil or military office. This was a severe blow to Catholics hoping to make a career or improve their prospects in life.

The next year an Act of Uniformity was passed, making it compulsory to use the Anglican Book of Common Prayer in all religious services, which made it difficult both for us Catholics and for those Dissenters who preferred their own, much simpler forms of service. Later, in 1664, the Conventicle Act forbade unauthorised religious meetings of five or more people who were not of the same household thus emphasising that it was illegal for us to gather for the Roman Mass.

In spite of these setbacks, in Staffordshire the Catholic faith continued strongly, with many Catholic families in favour with the King although several faced difficulties from anti-papist laws. In 1675 Lord Aston of Staffordshire protested to King Charles that many of those families such as the Penderels or Whitgreaves, who had been so loyal in their Preservation of the King, were now being prosecuted for practising their Faith. My father and Mr. Charles Giffard worked hard to bring their plight before the King. His Majesty, in loyalty to his friends, had the proceedings against Thomas Whitgreave and his nephew Francis Reynolds stopped as well as the charges for recusancy against the Penderel brothers, Mary Penderel and Elizabeth Yates.

No doubt he remembered well the kindnesses they had administered to him in his hour of need. When I saw my father again in later years he showed me proudly a copy of the proposal from the House of Lords;

Giffard, Penderells, & al. to be exempted from Laws against Papists

ORDERED, by the Lords Spiritual and Temporal in Parliament assembled, That Mr. Charles Giffard, Francis Yates and his Wife, William Penderell, John Penderel, Richard Penderel, Humphrey Penderel, and George Penderel,

Mr. Thomas Whitgreave of Moseley, Colonel William Carlos, and Mr. Francis Reynolds of Carleton in the County of Bedford, who were instrumental in the Preservation of His Majesty's Person after the Battle at Worcester, or such of them as are now living, shall, for their said Service, live as freely as any of His Majesty's Protestant Subjects, without being liable or subject to the Penalties of any of the Laws relating to Popish Recusants; and that a Bill be prepared and brought into this House for that Purpose, and the Name of Mr. John Huddleston be inserted therein.

From: 'House of Lords Journal Volume 13: 7 December 1678', Journal of the House of Lords: volume 13: 1675-1681

Thus King Charles remembered his Staffordshire friends and it became easier for them to practise their Catholic Faith without fear of fines or their property being confiscated, in their home area where he had been sheltered by them.

My Life as a Priest

The Jesuits, to whom I now belonged, were strongly established in the county of Staffordshire, and I longed to finish my training and join them. Howsoever, the formation of Jesuits is very long. When I went to Messina I was in the Novitiate for two years, learning to be part of the Community and taking part in the Thirty Days of Spiritual Exercises, laid down by our founder, Ignatius Loyola. At the end of those two years I took three vows, of poverty, chastity and obedience. For three years after that I studied theology and philosophy and engaged in some ministerial work. From 1660 I spent three years teaching in schools and university followed by another three years of formal theological studies preparing for my ordination as a priest.

What joy and excitement I felt as I approached England once more, ready to serve as a priest, meaning to live my life according to the example of the blessed John Southworth. But I was not called to be as heroic as he was. The work given to me was teaching for the College of the Holy Apostles, which was the Suffolk District of mission for the Roman Catholic Church in England. There was danger enough in being a priest in England, saying Mass in private houses and administering Confession and the Last Rites to the sick and dying, but I never endured the hardships and imprisonments that Southworth had suffered.

It was the custom for Catholic priests to assume an alias, in order to avoid being known by the authorities. I worked under the name of Dorrington. They were a family in Stafford, whom I had much admired, being Catholic and the original builders of the High House in Stafford, where my father had been imprisoned for a few months during the Civil War.

Working in the Suffolk and Essex area, I was given board and shelter by the generous Wright family at Kelvedon Hall. John Wright had been influenced by the composer William Byrd, who lived nearby at Stondon Massey. Byrd not only wrote heavenly music to the glory of God, but also witnessed his Catholic Faith to others. The Wright family converted to Catholicism and Byrd was charged with having led them astray. The Wrights kept a secret chapel in their house and a room for me to lodge; thus it is that I have a pleasant, quiet place to live in the peace of the Essex countryside, unlike my exemplar Southworth, who spent his life in the noxious slums of London among the very poorest people.

One tragedy that befell my family caused me, my father and my mother grievous sorrow. My brother Thomas, nine years younger than I, having moved to London to work with my father in his business interests there, succumbed to illness in the year of the deadly Plague that decimated that city in 1665. Thomas was very young, just twenty-five years old, and it pained me that I had spent so little time with him, having left to accompany my father when he was just a child, and only seeing him on rare occasions thereafter. For my father there was an added sadness, that now there would be no descendants for him, as I was a priest sworn to celibacy. Poor Thomas was buried in Fulham All Saints church, and commemorated with a fine tombstone, bearing our Carlos family coat of arms. My mother grieved for him for the rest of her life until she too passed away in the summer of 1676. She was laid to rest in the quiet country churchyard of St Philip and St James, near the fine house that my father had purchased at Hallow in Worcestershire, on 26th June.

Remaining in King Charles' high esteem, my father had been appointed a Gentleman of the Privy Chamber, in 1666. This meant that he was attending the King in his private rooms and present at important appointments, meetings and entertainments, as well as being paid a generous salary. I was proud of him, being content to see him so honoured. In the highest circles of genteel society, he was recognised as the man who had shielded his Sovereign with loyalty and valour. Accounts of the adventure of the Royal Escape were written and circulated, one of them the personal recollections of the King himself. My own dear father was acknowledged as a hero.

There were always some factions however who resented Catholics, or who were suspicious, believing that England was under threat from the great Continental Catholic nations of France or Spain. When the disastrous fire destroyed much of London it was widely believed that Papists had plotted it. At times public opinion against the Roman Catholics became dangerously bitter.

Plots and Intrigues against Catholics

It is the method of the Jesuits, in these present times, to proselytize a country that is not Catholic, such as England, and divide it into areas known as missions or residences. Soon after Charles was restored, there were eleven Jesuits living and working in the county of Staffordshire and the mission became known as the College of St. Chad. There are about seven working there now, and in August of this year of 1678, there was a most joyous gathering at Boscobel, of priests and gentry, to celebrate the taking of final vows by John Gavan, who had worked for the church in Wolverhampton.

Richard Vavasour was there, with Robert Petre, Francis Evers, (Lord Aston's chaplain at Tixall), Edward Leveson and William Ireland. These priests were all from old, staunchly Catholic families. More than twenty recusant gentlemen joined them, including Walter Heveningham of Aston, Walter Fowler, Sir James Simeon and Robert Howard of Hoar Cross. How I longed to be there with them, but my teaching and priestly duties, as well as increasingly poor health, kept me in Essex during that long, hot August. After the service and the profession of Gavan's vows, the whole company went to view the famous oak where my father had hidden with the King, and afterwards they dined on venison and drank the health of His Majesty.

But there were some mischievous people who were spreading lies and rumours against Catholics in England, especially in accusations against the Jesuits. It was whispered to King Charles that Louis XIV of France and the Jesuits were conspiring to assassinate him and to conquer England. The Queen's physician, Sir George Wakeman, and the Duchess of York's secretary, Edward Coleman, were accused of being involved. Soon the news was spread about and increasing numbers of Catholics, including five Catholic peers, among them Lord Stafford and Lord Aston, were named as plotters. It is all false but ignorant people are ready to believe the worst lies that vicious tongues repeat.

These last few months, all London has been gripped by fear and hysteria, believing that the French and the Spanish are about to invade, and treat Protestants cruelly, as the French rulers did with the Huguenots. The rogue behind this false calumny is a man called Titus Oates, who once trained with the Jesuits, but, probably being recognised for the scoundrel that he was, left them and is now pointing an accusing finger at as many Catholics as he is able to. Many good people are being arrested and brought for trial, and no doubt some will be put to death unjustly. I am told I am on his list, but being very ill now, I am unlikely to be arrested before I die.

I am sorry that my father may experience some anxiety of being implicated, having a Jesuit son, but I am reassured by the fact that His Majesty has complete trust in him. The King has shown himself able to defend those he loves and trusts, taking all measures to refute accusations against his Queen and Father John Huddleston. But I fear there will be some he cannot save from execution.

It seems my illness will cause me to avoid the scaffold; I will not undergo the agony of a brutal, public death but I suffer daily discomfort and pain, and may do so for some months to come. I offer all my sufferings up in union with those of my Beloved Saviour, Jesus Christ, and I look forward to seeing Him, in His Infinite Mercy. Great comfort is given to me by the care and tender nursing of Mary, a good woman who has been employed to look after me, by the kindness of the Wright family. My poor father, I fear, will be caused great sorrow by my death. It is hard for a man to lose both sons and be left without issue. If it pleaseth God that I should see him before I die, I will thank my father for teaching me fortitude, steadfastness and an abiding love for our religion. I have always tried to follow his example; whereas he sheltered the King in a tree and saved the monarchy for England, I, (along with scores of other priests), kept alive the practice of the Mass and protected the Catholic Faith in England.

Now as my strength is failing, and my life ebbing away, I am borne up by the words of Saint Paul, often quoted to us in the seminary:

"Pray that the Lord's message may spread quickly and be received with honour as it was among you; and pray that we may be preserved from the interference of bigoted and evil people, for faith is not given to everyone. But the Lord is faithful and He will give you strength, and guard you from the evil one, and we, in the Lord, have every confidence that you are doing, and will go on doing, all that we tell you."

The Lord indeed is faithful; with great joy this day I received word that I have been granted the privilege of taking my final vows, to raise me to full fellowship in the Society of Jesus. Although it is twenty-five years since I journeyed to Rome and have been ordained a priest for some time, there have been some delays due to the circumstances of these troublesome times, and so it is only now that I can take my final vows. I feel unworthy, but I suspect my superior is granting dispensation because he knows I am near my end. Tomorrow I will renew my promises of chastity, obedience and poverty and add the fourth Jesuit vow of obedience to the Pope, as well as five minor vows. A few fellow Jesuits will pray and rejoice with me. Then I will indeed be ready to place myself in the presence of My Saviour. I hope that I have lived to the best of my ability in the spirit of the prayer written by our Founder, Ignatius;

"Teach us good Lord,
To serve you as you deserve,
To give and not to count the cost,
To fight and not to heed the wounds,
To toil and not to seek for rest,
To labour and not ask for any reward,
Save that of knowing that we do your will. Amen."

If I have lived in that way at all, it is thanks to my beloved father Colonel William Careless, who guided me with his ideals of devoted loyalty and selflessness, and gave me courage, whenever mine faltered.

* * *

[Tears came to Ellen's eyes as she listened to the priest's account of his life and his testimony to his father. Such idealism and difficulties, bravery and suffering, dedication and physical frailty seemed to her to be heroic to the point of saintliness. Father Carlos was helped back to a seat in the shadows at the side of the room by the last two witnesses, who then came forward together to speak to Ellen. The young well-dressed yeoman and the old grey-haired priest stood side by side to tell their story together. First Edward spoke and then Father John Huddleston himself, taking turns to explain the last years of the Colonel's life.]

CHAPTER 8

Testimony of Edward Carlos, Apothecary of Worcester, adopted son of Colonel William Carlos

From my earliest youth I had known of my famous great uncle, William Careless, my grandfather's adventurous brother, who would appear unexpectedly at times at the family home, Broom Hall, wearing fine clothes and telling us all about his life in the exalted circles of London. The story of his hiding with the King in the oak tree was told to us children over and over again, and became part of our games, re-enacted many times, embellished and embroidered in our imaginations.

My father's cousins, the Colonel's sons William and Thomas, were many years older than me. Much of the time they had dwelt with my grandfather's family at Broom Hall, except for the time they were at Lapley during the War or at the castle of Tong when their father was governor there. William was serious, studious and very devout in the practice of his Faith; it did not surprise any of his family or relations that he took the decision to be a priest. The younger Thomas, I was told, died tragically in London when I was less than a year old.

When I was fifteen, my family suffered many months of fear and tension as rumours flew on every side that Catholics were suspected of vile and treacherous plots to overthrow the King and Government. Titus Oates spread dozens of dangerous accusations, and even our good neighbours who knew us well, for a while looked at us with suspicion. Officials would come knocking on the doors of suspected papists, asking questions about the practice of our religion; they were sent by Zachary Babington, the deputy clerk of the peace in Staffordshire, who had been ordered by the County M.P. Sir Walter Bagot to conduct a survey of how many people were Recusants in the area. I remember how my mother and father were full of fear and dread, but our home at Broomhall being remote, we escaped attention.

This was fortunate for they would have had to admit they had often not attended the services in the nearby Anglican Church in Brewood but had gone furtively to Mass in local gentry's houses. It would have been very tempting to hide the truth, but as well as being too principled to lie, or deny their faith, they thought that neighbours in any case might speak plainly about them and give them away. The list of Recusants that nosy officials drew up in 1680 included over fifteen hundred Catholics in Staffordshire, including almost a score of priests.

My uncle William came to visit us, judging it wise to be away from Court at such a time of suspicion and scare-mongering. He told us that accusations were being hurled against dozens of people; William Howard, the Viscount of Stafford was arrested and impeached, along with four other elderly Catholic Lords, Arundel, Powis, Petre and Belayse. Even the Queen and the King's brother, James Duke of York were accused of planning to bring foreign Catholic powers in to take over the country. His Majesty had refused to allow any action against his irreproachably virtuous wife, told his brother to go abroad for a while out of danger, and was said to have laughed out loud at the ridiculous notion of one of the Catholic nobles, the aged Lord Arundel, being a commander of insurgent forces.

Neither would the King allow any action to be taken against Father John Huddleston, the Queen's chaplain, for he remembered well the time he had spent at Moseley in that good man's company, in the desperate days when he was in hiding after Worcester. In a bid to calm the frenzy against Catholics, in April 1680 King Charles issued a proclamation forbidding the celebration of events with bonfires, without the permission of the Privy council or the magistrates of London, because the Faction were turning them into an occasion of stirring up tumults and dangerous sedition, attacking any unfortunate Catholics they could find. In consequence Charles' birthday on 29th May was celebrated with other forms of merrymaking but without bonfires. On the annual day for burning the Pope in effigy, since they were not allowed to burn their effigy, they decided to throw it into the river but while the statue was being made ready, perhaps through the carelessness of the workmen, who may even have been drunk, the house in which it was being prepared caught fire and was reduced to ashes, as were also two hundred and fifty other houses. This avenging fire expiated the wickedness of the earlier bonfires and punished the City for its former sinful fires.

In May Charles also forbade Gazettes, or papers giving news of the day, to appear or be distributed without his permission, because of the many false reports likely to upset the populace and disturb the peace of the realm, which were being disseminated through them.

We were disturbed to hear that Lord Aston, one of the leaders of the Catholic community in our part of Staffordshire, had been arrested and incarcerated in The Tower of London, on suspicion of involvement with the alleged plot against the King. He had a fine mansion at Tixall, about twelve miles away from us, and in the November of 1678, having just succeeded to the estate after the death of his father in April, he dismissed his bailiff, Stephen Dugdale, who had been embezzling his money. Being thrown out of employment, sly and vengeful, this scurrilous Dugdale began to spread rumours and statements that led to the condemnation of Lord Stafford and Father Ireland.

Dugdale maintained that many conversations had taken place at Tixall about Catholicism being restored in England; he stated that plots were discussed about killing the King and his illegitimate son the Duke of Monmouth. Lord Stafford, he claimed, had been at Lord Aston's home frequently, with Jesuits coming and going; he said that Lord Stafford had offered Dugdale bribes to join in with the plot. The August meeting at Boscobel, to ordain the Jesuit John Gavan, was represented as a clandestine gathering of Jesuits and the local Staffordshire gentry, in order to discuss treason.

Four of the gentlemen who had been at Boscobel were brought before the Committee of Examinations to be questioned closely, but thankfully it was believed that their patronising of priests was not treacherous, and they were allowed to go home. The news flew around our neighbourhood that Tixall Hall was searched twice, but nothing incriminating was found.

The overwhelming fear that troubled my uncle was that his son, now working as a Jesuit priest down in Essex, would be imprisoned, tortured and even executed. However, illness meant that my cousin William was spared arrest and his death that cold January, though lamentable, was more merciful than a brutal hanging at Tyburn.

The loss of his dear son grieved my uncle exceedingly, especially as now he had no descendants or heirs, and hence because he had always had a great affection for me, he took the idea into his mind that he should make me his adopted son. I was deeply honoured to be associated with him in this way and I resolved to strive to be worthy of his memory and the heroic ideals for which he stood.

The Titus Oates Malignity

FR. JOHN GAWEN (*alias* GAVAN), S.J
MARTYR FOR THE FAITH.
Suffered at Tyburn, June 30, 1679.

Many priests were arrested or on the run in 1679. We were troubled when we heard that William Atkins, Robert Petre and Francis Cotton, all Jesuits, had been arrested. John Gavan, who had taken his final vows at Boscobel the August before amidst so much rejoicing, was betrayed by an apostate priest, Schibber, and arrested on 29 January.

He eloquently defended himself and four other fellow priests when they were tried at the Old Bailey, but the principal of the trial was that no Catholic could be believed, and he was brutally hanged, drawn and quartered at Tyburn on 20 June, 1679.

One of the sons of the Leveson family, Francis died in prison and Gregory Farmer, who was connected to Lord Stafford, was put into Stafford gaol, where he died later in 1685. At least eight other priests were in hiding or trying to escape to the Continent. These dedicated men had spent their lives serving us, doing God's work; they did not deserve such punishments.

My uncle William, on one of his visits to our home, told us how distressing it was for him to see his former acquaintance Lord Stafford led into Westminster Hall to be tried by his peers, nearly two years after his arrest. Known to us as William Howard, he was at this time sixty-eight years old, deaf and with poor eyesight. Denied counsel from any lawyer, he had to conduct his own defence.

"The poor man, unable to hear properly the evidence offered against him by foul perjurers, often became confused, and he failed to offer some of the arguments that may have saved him," declared my Uncle. "I, like many others, had often found him to be short tempered and disagreeable, but he was always honest, and devoted to his own wife and children. He hoped, like many of us, for the chance to say our prayers in our own way and be free to hear Mass, but he never plotted violence to bring it about, or to threaten the King. Some of his own relatives, who were amongst the peers, betrayed him by voting him guilty. The King was angry with those who had condemned him, but had to sign the warrant for his execution, though with tears in his eyes."

"Stafford was executed on 29 December, 1680. One thing the King had been able to do was to prevent him being hung, drawn and quartered, but instead to be beheaded, a more merciful way to die. He made a dignified impression on those who had come to see his death, stating his innocence and expressing his love for his family."

I thought my dear Uncle appeared older as he related this account to us. By this time, he was about seventy years old, and had been worn with much worry these last few years because of the troubles resulting from Titus Oates' plot.

Lord Aston thankfully did not suffer execution, but he was imprisoned in the Tower for six, long years, not being released until 1685. The anti-Catholic hysteria began to die down as Oates was discredited, it being realized that his evidence was lies and falsehoods. He was deprived of his government pension, then in 1684, we rejoiced to hear that he was arrested at a coffee-house in London and tried by the feared Judge Jeffreys, and, as he was unable to pay the huge fine imposed on him of £100,000, he was put into irons in prison, a punishment that we Catholics felt he deserved, in return for all the unjust imprisonments that he had brought about and the brutal deaths that he had caused.

The Death of the King

The Duke of York, the King's brother, came back from exile and was allowed to take his place once more in the Privy Council. Because he had become Catholic and married a Catholic princess, Mary of Modena, we had high hopes a bettering of our situation when he should become King, but our very hopes were, on the contrary, a cause of great fear for the Protestants in England.

On a rain swept February day in 1685 the news came that his Majesty King Charles II had died. The dark young man, in desperate danger, good humoured in the face of all manner of hardships and always considerate of the humble people risking their lives for him, who had hidden in our remote part of quiet Staffordshire all those years ago, had now passed away to a more eternal Kingdom, ruled by a higher King than himself.

* * *

[After Edward spoke, the elderly priest, John Huddleston, took his turn to speak, eager to give his account of how he had at last received King Charles into the Holy Roman Catholic Church.]

CHAPTER 9

Testimony of Father John Huddleston & Edward Carlos, Apothecary of Worcester

I think he had been in sympathy with our Church from the time of his stay with us. I mind well how we talked at Moseley Hall, during the two or three days that he was sheltered by us there. At my first sight of him my heart was touched by how worn out and bedraggled he looked, dressed in old country style clothes, his feet in a dreadful state, his hair cropped short and his hands stained brown. I bathed his feet as indeed William Careless had done a few days previously and gave him a new shirt from one of mine own and warm stockings for his feet.

During the days when he was waiting and hiding, he asked me about what we Catholics believed. He asked to see the little Oratory in the upstairs garret, assuring me that he knew I was a priest and I should not fear to admit it to him, for if it pleased God to restore him to his kingdom, he would make it so that we need not have to hide anymore. When I showed him a Catechism, and a tract written by my uncle, 'A Short and Plain Way to the Faith and the Church', he studied them with interest and remarked that he had not seen anything more plain and clear upon that subject and that the arguments about the succession of the Church from the Apostles were conclusive and undeniable.

I admit that I was disappointed when Charles became King that he did not improve the situation for Catholics in England as much as had been hoped by us. I believe that in his heart he often felt drawn towards the Church of his mother but knew it would endanger his hold on the throne and cause great divisions throughout the realm. I know that he was admiring of the example that Colonel Careless gave of a quiet but sincere belief. I myself had known William Careless and his family for many years, often administering the Sacraments to them clandestinely. Charles saw his loyalty, his readiness to serve in spite of all risks and his thoughtfulness for others; as indeed he had encountered in all the Catholics around Boscobel who had worked together to preserve his safety in his hour of need.

It was only in the last few days of his life that Charles felt free to admit his true longings. His brother James, who was in the dying King's room, asked him if he would like to see a priest, and he answered that he would, with all his heart. By the hand of Providence, I was nearby in Queen Catherine's suite of rooms, and I was brought secretly to a closet which led to the King's chamber and told to wait there. Not having had the chance to bring the Holy Sacrament, I asked one of the Queen's Portuguese priests, Fr. Bento de Lemoz, to go to fetch a consecrated Host from St. James. Soon I was brought into the presence of the King, who cried out in joy to see me,

> "You once saved my body, and now you have come to save my soul!"

(Father Huddleston continued in his simple, unaffected way describing the scene that followed.)

I asked the King what service I could perform for the happiness of his soul, and he declared he desired to die in the Faith and communion of the holy Catholic Church. He was heartily sorry for his sins, forgave his enemies and desired pardon for all those he had in anywise offended. I offered to give him the sacrament of penance, and he proceeded to make an exact confession of his whole life, with exceeding compunction and tenderness of heart. He repeated with me a simple Act of Contrition, ending,

> "Into thy hands, sweet Jesus, I commend my soul. Mercy, sweet Jesus, mercy."

After I had given him absolution, I asked him if he would like to receive Holy Communion, and he replied,

> "By all means. I desire to be partaker of all the helps necessary for my condition. If I am worthy, pray fail not to let me have it."

By the time I had anointed him the holy Sacrament had been brought to his door and was delivered to me. As I brought it over to him, he struggled to raise himself up, saying,

> "Let me meet my heavenly Lord in better posture than in my bed."

But I entreated him to rest where he was. God Almighty, who saw all men's hearts, would accept his good intention. The King then received Communion with all the symptoms of devotion imaginable. This done, I prayed for a few more minutes, recommending his soul to God.

> "May God receive your soul into his blessed hands; and after this transitory world, grant you a joyful resurrection, and an eternal crown of glory in the next."

I left him then, in a very peaceful frame of mind. It was one of the most joyfully rewarding experiences of my life to bring King Charles into our Church and his soul into union with the Lord Our Saviour. One more long night he lingered, and then the next day at noon, with his family all around him, he died. I thank God that He has used me as his humble instrument to receive the King, for there were several other priests, belonging to the court of Queen Catherine, more learned and exalted in rank than I. But being Portuguese, they may not have understood his speech as well as I did and he felt at ease with me, who had shared his dangers and fears all those years ago.

Father John Huddleston.

(As Father Huddleston finished his narration, Edward took up his story once more, remembering the moment when the old priest had come to Broom Hall to describe the King's deathbed scene to the Careless family living there.)

We bowed our heads in a moment of silence, and prayed for the soul of King Charles, who, in spite of imperfections and disappointments, had not forgotten his Staffordshire friends. My uncle Colonel William Carlos in particular, had been rewarded with various benefits, and had been kept close in friendship to King Charles, being honoured to be a Gentleman of the Royal Bedchamber.

And thus it was that my Uncle passed from long and loyal service to King Charles, to working for the new King, James II.

Serving Another King

I asked my Uncle William on his next visit to Broom Hall, how he fared in this new situation.

"It must be a great joy and relief for you, Uncle, to at last serve a Catholic monarch, and to be able to acknowledge your faith openly after so many years of being forced to be discreet," I began. The worthy old soldier thought for a while before he answered me.

"All these years I have indeed looked forward to such a situation, though not for a moment did I swerve in my loyalty to King Charles. Because I had sheltered him when he was in mortal danger, there was always the most deep and special friendship between us. However, like all Catholics I longed for a day when we could practise our religion without fear of reprisals. But now that time has come, I have some fears for King James. I have known him for many years; I remember well several times fighting alongside him in warfare, especially at the Battle of the Dunes where he showed great bravery. There is no doubting his personal courage, both as a soldier and in his principles. He was not afraid to convert to Catholicism although it was not wise for his political position."

"Why I am anxious for him is that, unlike his brother Charles, he is unwilling to bend when the wind blows, and aims to put forward his own policies without understanding how deeply held the views of others are. He aims to restore rights to Catholics in England, which for my part I would be glad of, but he does not realize how entrenched and suspicious most Protestants in Parliament, the gentry and the Church of England are, against what they regard as papists. English people distrust the influence of foreign powers, from the time of the Spanish Armada to the present Louis of France. They still remember the Gunpowder Plot and the great fire of London, which some blamed on us Catholics. Most English people are content with their Bible in English and their Book of Common Prayer and being used to their services in their own language, they fear they will have Latin forced upon them. We may know that their fears are groundless, but suspicion has been ground deep into their way of thinking for generations now."

"At first things seemed promising. There was no damaging opposition to James taking the throne, and he told Parliament that he would protect the Church of England. The House of Commons is quite loyal to the throne and was ready to give him a fair chance. But he can be unfortunately high-handed in his dealings with the House, and when they asked him to issue a proclamation enforcing the laws against all dissenters from the Church of England, he was angry. He intended, on the contrary, to create civic equality for Catholics, Protestant Dissenters and Anglicans. Can you imagine that? What a step forward for our nation and society! There would be freedom to worship in our different ways without obstruction to our careers or education or owning land. For it must be difficult too for those Protestants who are more puritanical than the Church of England; they in common with us suffer imprisonment, such as that writer Bunyan, who was gaoled for twelve years for preaching, just because he was only a layman, not a clergyman. However, I do not think either the Church of England or Parliament is likely to agree willingly to allow such a change."

Although my Uncle was getting on in years, he was still working for the King, though in what way I am not sure, for he would say very little about his role. In later years I learned that he was paid £300 from King James' secret service, so I understood he might gather information about those who might threaten the King; regrettably, there were many such people.

As for me, farming had held no great interest for me, and thus when it came time for me to seek some occupation, I set my mind on learning the trade of apothecary, leaving the family home at Broomhall and settling in Worcester. It was strange to go to a city that held so many associations and fearful memories for my uncle, but he was a pragmatic, stoical soldier who shrugged off the defeats or failures of war. He had even bought this house where I now live, two or three miles out of Worcester, near a small hamlet called Hallow. I was fortunate that I married my beloved wife Dorothy who is the daughter and heiress of Thomas Smith of Quenibor- ough in Leicestershire, and we have been blessed with several children.

That June of 1685, we were disturbed to hear that rebellions had broken out against James, in Scotland led by the Marquis of Argyll and in the West Country by the Duke of Monmouth, who was an illegitimate son of Charles II. Thankfully, King James was able to put them down without too much difficulty, but he was shaken by these disturbances and decided to push for more officers who would be loyal to him, by suspending the Test Act, so that Catholics could serve as officers in the navy and army. The Commons protested against this and neither did they approve of his wish to suspend penal laws against Nonconformists. Everything that James did seemed to cause more opposition to him both in Parliament and in the established Anglican Church.

There was great rejoicing amongst us Catholics when King James restored Catholic bishops to England, though they were called Vicars Apostolic, because each diocese already had an Anglican bishop. The country was divided into four large areas: London, the Northern, the Western and the Midland district. There had been no Confirmations since the reign of the old King James I, and so it was a great occasion for us when Doctor John Leyburn arrived in the Midlands in October 1687.

He made a great tour around, Confirming over twenty thousand people over the course of some weeks, and came to Stafford to the chapel in Eastgate Street, which had recently been built by Daniel Fitter, one of two brothers from a respectable Wolverhampton family. Having trained abroad in Lisbon and Paris, this Daniel Fitter was chaplain to the Fowler family at St. Thomas near Stafford. During the time of danger from Titus Oates plot, he had been forced to go to the Continent for safety but had now returned.

On 2 October, two hundred and nineteen souls were able to reaffirm their adherence to the Holy Catholic Church, in Stafford chapel, an event undreamed of in the reigns of previous monarchs. Five more were confirmed at St. Thomas, and thirty-seven in the town at Wolverhampton; here the Jesuits had a fine chapel and a school for nearly fifty boys. The mood amongst the Catholics of our area was of joy and liberation after the long years of prohibition and secrecy. How strange it seemed to be worshipping in large numbers, singing and praying in a church in the town, openly and freely, rather than a small secret group huddled quietly and fearfully in a hidden attic. What the townspeople of Stafford made of it I am not sure. Some in the street around stared at us dubiously, some impassively, but apart from a few mutterings of disapproval, no real aggression was offered.

The next April, in 1688, we were further elated to hear that Bonaventure Giffard had been appointed to be Vicar General in our Midland District. He of course was one of the well-respected Giffard family who had been the mainstay and protectors of Catholicism in our area for generations. A member of the branch of the family who lived in Cock Street in Wolverhampton, his father had been Andrew Giffard who died fighting for Charles I during the Civil War. They were a remarkably religious family, for Bonaventure had two brothers, Augustine and Andrew, who were also priests, and a sister Catherine who became a nun. He had studied to be a priest at Douai in the Spanish Lowlands and came to work as a priest in England in 1678 but was forced to seek refuge in France during the time of the Titus Oates persecution.

Now he was back, able to minister among his own people again. King James thought highly of him, for he had also been appointed a royal chaplain and preacher and was put in charge as president of Magdalen College, Oxford, which the King was intending to turn into a Catholic seminary.

That spring and early summer it seemed to us that the Catholic Faith in England would return from the wintry years of suppression and blossom once more. But alas! All too brief and all too fleeting, the flowering was destroyed, as though from a harsh frost in May. The Protestants of England were becoming increasingly alarmed, angry and in disagreement with King James. The Church of England did not like it when he tried to prevent their clergy from attacking the beliefs of the Catholic Church from their pulpits, and many were angry when the Bishop of London was suspended for doing so.

Nor did they agree with the Declaration of Indulgence which aimed at complete religious toleration and which the Anglican clergy were instructed to read aloud in their churches. Protestants in the army and navy were suspicious about the appointments of Catholic officers, whom they regarded as likely to have some allegiance to foreign powers; and Protestants in political positions were afraid that James was too much like his father, aiming to gather absolute powers to himself.

My uncle's fears about James' high-handedness were realized. For instance, in our own county town of Stafford, when James had granted a new borough charter, he had declared his right to remove officers and members of the corporation. He appointed a Catholic to fill a vacancy among the aldermen, a Doctor Benjamin Thornburgh, who when he was elected to be mayor, was dispensed by the King from taking the oaths of allegiance and supremacy. A great disagreement arose when, in May 1688, James dismissed some aldermen and burgesses, the town clerk, the recorder and even the high steward, and nominated who should replace them. The town was in uproar and His Majesty had to back down, reinstating those he had dismissed, but I do not think the townspeople of Stafford forgave him and they did not support him when revolution threatened again.

In that summer of 1688 every news report that we heard from London was concerning clashes between the King and his opponents. The Archbishop of Canterbury and six other Bishops petitioned him against the Declaration of Indulgence. They said the sovereign had no right to do away with the penal code against religious dissidents. James was so angry he put the seven bishops on trial before the King's Bench, but they were acquitted and the people of London celebrated their release with great jubilation.

The fears of Protestants had greatly increased when it became known that the King's Catholic wife, Mary of Modena, was pregnant. Until now it had seemed she was not likely to bear a child but this time she was able to give birth to a healthy baby boy, on 10 June of that fateful year. Now it seemed that the monarchy would continue as Catholic for another generation, which we Catholics in our community rejoiced at greatly, but Protestants looked to the continent and saw the absolute power of Catholic monarchs such as Louis IV of France and were afraid that all the liberties and powers that Parliament had won through the bitter Civil War, would be lost.

I believe it was during these days that the Bishop of London and half a dozen others secretly invited William of Orange to come from Holland to take over from James. This ambitious prince had married King James' daughter Mary, who like her sister Anne, had been brought up as Protestant. The two princesses were daughters of King James from his previous marriage to Anne Hyde. Mary would be an acceptable claimant to the throne for the Protestants, who were now setting ridiculous rumours about, that the new baby was not the real son of James but had been smuggled into the Queen's birthing chamber in a warming pan.

My uncle told me that during that summer, King James spent much time and effort trying to form a Parliament that would repeal the penal laws and the Test Acts so that there would be freedom of conscience and toleration, for he was realizing that it would not be accepted if it was imposed by himself as sovereign. But time was running out for him. Prince William eagerly accepted the chance to take the throne of England. He sailed with a huge fleet, through the English Channel along the coast to Devon.

Large numbers of people watched it from their coastal homes and when he landed at Brixham, on 5th November (by custom an ill-day for Catholics) bands played to greet him. He was cleverly representing himself as the Saviour of Protestantism, the champion in Europe against the absolutist tyrant Louis of France. A printing press was set up to flood the public with leaflets about how he was going to save them from the spectre of Papistry. I heard that at Exeter he made his appearance on a white horse, like the one foretold in the Book of Revelation who was to crush evil. There were two hundred black Africans, from the Dutch colonies, marching with him and many banners were waved proclaiming that he was for God and the Protestant religion. No wonder that most Englishmen saw him as a hero, come to save them, rather than what he really was, a usurper and invader.

James tried to stop him, but some of his army officers deserted him and the navy went over to William's side. At the crucial moment James was taken ill, his nose pouring with blood, and he lost his nerve.

"It was the saddest thing I have ever seen in all my years of being a soldier," commented my Uncle William. "He had always been so brave, so fearless in battle. But he is not only older now, but as well as that, he felt bereft of support from his soldiers, his people, his Parliament and even from his own daughters."

Perhaps James was reluctant to begin a civil war again, remembering the devastation it brought to his people a generation ago. He gave up, sent his Queen and their child abroad, and fled from London. Trying to board a ship, he was caught and brought back to London, but William allowed him to escape again, and by Christmas Day he had arrived in France, scene of his exile with his brother so many years before. But this time there would be no glorious Restoration.

My uncle was exceedingly downcast by these events. All his life he had fought or worked for the Stuart monarchy, hoping and believing that through them there would be a place for Catholicism in England once more; but now all hopes and dreams were dashed.

"The English prefer a Protestant Dutchman to their true Catholic King," he grumbled bitterly. "William will be offered the Crown to be held jointly with his wife Mary. Toleration is rejected, at least for Catholics. Mobs are attacking Catholic chapels; that fine chapel in Stafford and the school have been destroyed, and the one in Wolverhampton has been wrecked. Books have been burned in the market place and furnishings, altar, altar rails and pulpit pillaged. I heard that the riotous behaviour was so violent that a man was killed in the affray. Even the new Mass house in Birmingham has been destroyed by a mob. It was only built last year, with the generosity of

King James, and money from our beloved Queen Catherine, King Charles' widow."

"As soon as the people of that city heard William had landed in November, they felt free to pull it apart and plunder it, encouraged by Lord Dellamer, who is a bitter Protestant opposed to any sort of papistry."

"Our dear bishop Bonaventure Giffard has been imprisoned in Newgate Gaol. All the freedom we enjoyed under James is at an end and I fear it may be a hundred years or more before the Catholic Church in England will be allowed to exist openly once more."

I tried to comfort my uncle, telling him that the Church which Christ founded would surely survive, and that faith becomes stronger when it is tested. My words helped him somewhat, but the heart had gone out of him, and he dwelt upon what had been lost and how the next generation of our family would be held back.

"If our descendants wish to go to Mass they will be penalised and their priests thrown into prison. They will be barred from inheriting or buying land and suffer heavy taxes. Once again, they will be viewed with suspicion and mistrust by their neighbours. Denied from going to university, denied from holding office in the army or navy, what chances will they have of ever improving their lives?"

My uncle's health began to fail. He was by now nearing eighty and was brought low in spirits by the country's rejection of King James. He set about making his will, and told me that I, as his adopted son, would be the Executor of it. By December it was drawn up and he signed it on the 28th day of that month. Perhaps it was a little consolation to him that his will was officially dated during the reign of King James, though His Majesty was by that time in exile in France.

Living mostly at his pleasant country house in Greene Street in Hallow, my Uncle sometimes needed to go to London to settle his business affairs, and it was while he was in London in May of 1689, that he passed peacefully away. He was much missed and talked about by all who knew him; it was the end of an era, the death of the hero of the Royal Oak. So many accounts had been written about him and his adventure, the daring escape of the young King and the seasoned soldier. Not so many knew of his Catholic background and his priestly son.

It was thought most fitting that his body should be brought back to Brewood, the town nearest to the Boscobel area where his great adventure had taken place. He was laid to rest in the churchyard of St. Mary's church, where inside is the splendid tomb of good Sir John Giffard with his wife and several children. His burial was on the 28th May, just one day before Oak Apple Day, which is when we celebrate King Charles II coming back in procession to London, on his thirtieth birthday.

Colonel William Careless closed his long, kind and eventful life respected, beloved and lamented by all to whom he was known. The people of Brewood were proud to have such a celebrated person as one of their own and there was talk of putting a memorial plaque to his achievements in the church.

My family and I benefited greatly from my uncle's generosity. To me and my wife Dorothy he left all the houses and properties in Stafford which he had purchased from Mrs. Elizabeth Ironmonger, the widow of his friend Humphrey Ironmonger (the man who had helped him to make his getaway after Boscobel with money and a pass to travel.) We also have his house at Hallow, where we live now very comfortably with our large family of children. The money he received from Trinity House in London, after signing over his rights to ballast from the Thames, he asked to be paid to myself and my brothers, William, Thomas, Richard, Francis and John, and to my sisters Mary Foster, Elizabeth, Eleanor and Margaret Carlos. Five priests are to be given ten shillings apiece, a sign of my uncle's abiding wish to help the Church of his ancestors.

I can say with pride that I am related to William Careless, and his legacy to me was not only the house and property, but over and above that, association with the reputation of heroism and loyalty.

* * *

The locket with the miniature portrait of Colonel Careless. The inscription inside the lid reads;

"Renowned Carlos! Thow hast won the day
(Loyalty Lost) by helping Charles away,
From Kings-Blood-Thirsty-Rebels in a Night,
made black with Rage, of thieves, & Hells dispight
Live! King-Loved-Sowle thy fame be Euer Spoke
By all whilst England Beares a Royall Oake."

Epilogue

Late afternoon sunshine broke through the heavy clouds, brightening the shadowy room. The nine figures began to move away, gradually fading from sight. Dorothy put her hand trustingly on her brother-in-law's arm and he led her out of Boscobel towards their home at Broom Hall, followed by young Edward. The two soldiers, Leveson and Giffard, saluted their King respectfully, before striding out of the room. Richard Penderel bowed a little awkwardly as he left but Charles smiled at him and grasped his hand, as with a friend. The two priests, the Colonel's son and the King's confessor, strolled quietly out in the direction of Moseley Old Hall, to pray in the dusty, hidden attic chapel there.

King Charles went over to the fireplace and leant his arms on the mantelpiece for a moment, gazing down into the hearth, as if he were seeing again the leaping flames, the pan of sizzling mutton and could hear the laughter and jesting between himself the fugitive king and the steadfast Colonel. The evening sun brightened as it set, lighting up the room and making all the shadows disappear. The figure of the Merry Monarch faded away as Ellen opened her eyes.

Now she understood something of the character of man who had saved the King, as well as the others who had risked their lives and liberty for him. She jumped up from her chair and hurried out to the neat garden, past the pleasant little arbour on its mound, out through the gate into the field which had once been a coppice. A few minutes' walk brought her to the oak, a descendant of the original Majestic Oak which had sheltered the King of England and his most true and faithful servant, on that rainy September day in 1651.

* * *

What happened to them afterwards

Several persons mentioned in the narrative have an interesting history themselves; here follows what happened in their lives in later years.

Colonel Thomas Leveson

From his base at Dudley Castle, Leveson made several raids on neighbouring towns. At Christmas 1643 he sent troops to Aston Hall near Birmingham and Sir Thomas Holte was forced to surrender. In a raid on Birmingham his troops drove off 300 head of cattle. After his defeat at Dudley, Leveson went into exile at Bordeaux in France. He came under the patronage of the Prince of Conti who paid him 2000 livres for entertaining. He died 8 September 1652 and was buried in the church of St. Purgett. He left behind him furniture and two horses which were sold to pay for his funeral expenses.

Sir William Brereton

He was the Parliamentary military commander in Staffordshire. In 1643 he captured the town of Stafford with no opposition and then besieged Stafford Castle where Lady Stafford was obstinately holding out. She was not persuaded by his threats or promises and he wrote that she was being influenced by the pernicious advice of Jesuits. His troops burnt down many houses and buildings by the castle. Later in July when his force threatened again, the Royalist garrison evacuated and he was able to enter the castle, which he ordered to be demolished. From autumn 1644 he was involved in the prolonged siege of Chester, which finally surrendered to Parliamentary Army in January 1646. After the end of the first Civil War he was given, as a reward for his services, Eccleshall Castle in Staffordshire and Croydon Palace, the home of the Archbishop of Canterbury. However, he began to withdraw from public life and refused to be one of the judges of King Charles I in January 1649.

Croydon Palace was returned to Archbishop Juxon during the Restoration but Brereton was allowed to continue living there as a tenant until his death in April 1661. His writings of the Civil War provide detailed accounts of events he was involved in and provide fascinating detail for anyone wishing to read more first-hand evidence of the Civil War.

Reference
A Journal of the English Civil War, The Letter Book of Sir William Brereton, edited by Joseph McKenna, McFarland and Company Inc. Jefferson, N. Carolina.

James Stanley 7th Earl of Derby

When Charles II was progressing with his army from Scotland down through England in 1651, he appointed the Earl of Derby, James Stanley, to be commander of the troops in Lancashire and Cheshire. Derby landed at Wyre Water in Lancashire and proceeded to Warrington but he did not obtain the support of the Presbyterians because he refused to take the Covenant. He was defeated at the Battle of Wigan Lane and was wounded. He went on the run with Colonel Roscarrock and found shelter and aid at Boscobel, with the help of the Penderels. A week or so later he joined the King at Worcester and after the battle was in the party that accompanied him in his escape. He told Charles how he had been hidden by recusants, saying that "those people being accustomed to persecution and searches were most likely to have the readiest means and safest contrivances to preserve him later."

After leaving the King at Boscobel, Lord Derby headed north but was arrested at Nantwich. He was tried by court-martial at Chester, found guilty of treason and condemned to death. He tried to escape but was recaptured by Captain Hector Schofield and taken to Bolton to be executed because he was remembered and disliked there for his part in the Battle of Bolton. On the 15th October 1651 he was put to death publicly at the Market Cross in Churchgate near the Man and Scythe Inn, which was owned by his family. He was buried in Ormskirk church. James Stanley was said to be a man of deep religious feeling and of great nobility of character.

References
D. Craine, (1995), 'Manannan's Isle', The Manx Museum and National Trust (ISBN 978-0-901106-10-0).
Draper, Peter (1864), 'Defeat of Charles and Capture of James, Earl of Derby', The house of Stanley; including the soeges of Lathom House with notices of relative and co-temporary incidents, T. Hutton.

The Girl on the Doorstep at Worcester

This incident is based on a story that my aunt used to tell me. She said that when she was little her grandmother told her, that her grandmother remembered, that her grandmother told her, that her grandmother used to say she could remember back to when she was a very young girl she was standing on the doorstep during the battle of Worcester and saw blood running down the street from the soldiers who had been slain there. It is a fine example of oral tradition and folk memories!

William Hamilton 2nd Duke of Hamilton

He was the most senior of the Scottish Royalist exiles with Charles II at The Hague. He returned in 1650 and went to his estate on the Isle of Arran, then joined the Royalist invasion of England as a colonel of a regiment drawn mainly from his tenants. At the Battle of Worcester, he was badly wounded and held prisoner at the

Commandery, which had been Charles' headquarters but was taken over by the Parliamentary Army.

He wrote a very brave and touching letter to his wife, knowing that he was near death:

> "Dear Heart, You know I have long been labouring, though in great weakness to be prepared against this expected Change, and I thank God I find Comfort in it, in this my day of Trial; for my Body is not more weakened by my Wounds, than I find my Spirit Comforted and Supported by the infinite Mercies and great Love of my Blessed Redeemer, who will be with me to the end and in the end."

He went on to wish that the Lord would comfort her and his dear nieces, and commended her to take care of his children,

> "Let Your great work be to make them early acquainted with God, and their duties to Him;"

and he blessed her,

> "May the Comforts of the Blessed Spirits be ever near you in all your Straits and Difficulties."

He signed the letter,

> "Dear Heart,
> Your Own,
> Hamilton."

This young Royalist officer died a few days later and was buried in Worcester Cathedral. William Hamilton had no sons at his death and the dukedom of Hamilton devolved to his niece, Anne, who became Duchess of Hamilton in her own right.

[Facsimile copies of his letter can be bought at the Commandery shop, Sidbury in Worcester. One of the streets nearby is named after him, Hamilton Road.]

Edward Martin

Edward Martin was a servant at White Ladies. When they were frantically disguising the King, in the early hours of the morning after the Battle of Worcester, Edward gave his shirt to Charles to make him look like a working country man. After the Restoration Edward Martin sent a petition to King Charles reminding him of how he had helped by lending him his "noggen" shirt and also that he had met him in the woods where he was hiding with Richard Penderel. The King had asked who he was and Richard had said he was a tenant of White Ladies and need not be feared, whereupon the King desired him to be private and promised that if it should please Almighty God to settle him in his own again he would assuredly raise his fortune.

Edward was yet another example of one of the dozens of ordinary people who risked punishment to help the King.

Reference
Calendar State Papers Domestic, 1660.

Francis and Elizabeth Yates

Francis Yates was a servant to Charles Giffard and it was he who led King Charles and his party to White Ladies with his useful local knowledge. His wife Elizabeth was the sister of Richard Penderel's wife Mary and that is why when they arrived at White Ladies it was said that George Penderel, who answered the door, was his brother-in-law.

Elizabeth, the wife of Francis brought food to the King when he was hiding in Spring Coppice in the rain with Richard. Charles was not sure he could trust a woman, thinking that women like to gossip, but she assured him that she would die rather than give him away. Later when Charles needed money, Francis Yates offered to give him thirty shillings but the King would only accept ten. The King was reminded of this incident when Francis Yates' son petitioned him after the Restoration:

"His father, being sent by your Majesty to Mr. Giffard for money to supply your Majesty's needs, and missing Mr. Giffard, your petitioner's father, according to his duty, did deliver to your Majesty all the money he had, part of which your Majesty was graciously pleased to accept."

When the Penderel brothers accompanied King Charles through the woods to Moseley Old Hall, Francis Yates walked with them.

Francis was the only one of the many that helped the King in Staffordshire to be executed. He was arrested and questioned but would not tell the authorities where the King had gone. He was tried and hanged at Oxford.

After Charles was restored to the throne, a petition was presented to him from William Hardwick, a brother-in-law of Elizabeth Yates, reminding him of the sacrifice Francis had made and pointing out that Elizabeth was now a widow.

In 1664 she was granted an annuity of £50 each year for herself and for her son Richard and his heirs. Payments have continued to be made to the family ever since. She was also granted exemption from proceedings against her for recusancy, in company with Thomas Whitgreave and the Penderels, after a petition from Lord Aston in 1675.

There is some confusion because it seems there was another Francis Yates of Langley Lawn near White Ladies whose wife was Margaret Penderel, sister to the five Penderel brothers.

References
'An Exact Narrative and Relation of His Most Sacred Majesty's Escape from Worcester' published in 1660.
'Catholic Staffordshire' by Michael Greenslade, pages 114, 115, 120, 133, 135.

Lord Henry Wilmot

Henry Wilmot shared in the wanderings of Charles II after he arrived at Moseley. He had been guided by John Penderel to Colonel Lane's house at Bentley and was offered a pass to get to London, but when he heard that the King was still in the area he arranged that the King should have the pass, riding as a manservant for Colonel Lane's daughter Jane.

He was completely opposite in character to William Careless who was always discreet and aware of what would look suspicious. Wilmot was impulsive, refused to disguise himself and ignored the fact that he might be putting others in danger. It was more by luck than judgement that he managed to escape.

In exile with the King on the Continent, he was created Earl of Rochester in 1652. Returning to England in 1655 he attempted an uprising at Marston Moor as part of the Sealed Knot Penruddock uprising, but it was unsuccessful. He fled back to the Continent and the next year was put in command of an English foot regiment in the royalist army in Bruges. Many in that regiment fell sick the next winter because of its unhealthy and overcrowded conditions, including Wilmot himself; he died at Sluys on 19th February 1658 and was buried at Bruges.

His son, John Wilmot, became the 2nd Earl of Rochester and was a poet, libertine and writer of outrageous plays at the Court of Charles II during the Restoration.

It is interesting that of two men, who were close companions of the King in his famous Escape, one was the father of a priest and the other was the father of a drunken, debauched libertine.

References
C.H. Firth, Henry Wilmot, first Earl of Rochester, DNB, 1900.
R. Hutton, Henry Wilmot, first Earl of Rochester, DNB, 2004.
R. Ollard, The Escape of Charles II after the Battle of Worcester, 1966, Hodder and Stoughton.

Websites
www.britannica.com/biography/Henry-Wilmot-1st-Earl-of-Rochester.
www.cracroftspeerage.co.uk/online/content/rochester1652.htm.

Father John Huddleston

When James II became King, John Huddleston continued to live at the dowager Queen Catherine's residence at Somerset House. As he grew older his mind began to fail, and Queen Catherine, when she returned to Portugal in 1692, asked Lord Faversham, her lord Chamberlain, to look after him. He died at Somerset House in 1698 at the advanced age of ninety.

References
1. The tract written by his uncle Richard Huddleston, 'A Short and Plain Way to the Faith and the Church' which he had shown to King Charles at Moseley Hall, was published by Father John Huddleston in London in 1688. In the same volume were, 'Two papers written by the late King Charles' found in the King's closet after his death and 'A briefe account of Occurrences relating to the Miraculous Preservation of our Late Sovereign Lord King Charles II after the Defeat of his Army at Worcester in the Year 1651. Faithfully taken from the express testimony of those two worthy Roman Catholics Thomas Whitgreave Esq. and Mr John Huddleston, Priest of the order of St. Benet.'
2. www.catholic.org/encyclopedia.
3. William Salt Library at Stafford S.H.C. (Collections for a History of Staffordshire).
4. Staffordshire Catholic History Journal 14, pages 391-393, written by John Kirk (1760-1851) who was a historian and Catholic priest at Lichfield.

A brief history of the Careless [or Carlos] family

See the pedigree chart at the end of the illustrations

The following is a brief history of the Careless family and its association with Broom Hall as shown from the Giffard Estate papers which are at Stafford Record Office and Wills, previously located at Lichfield Record Office, but now moved to Stafford Record Office.

The Careless family were associated with Broom Hall near Brewood in Staffordshire since 1556, during the reign of Queen Mary, when Thomas Careless was a tenant of Broom Hall from Sir John Giffard. John and Ellen Careless and their son Edward were granted a lease of the lands that belonged to John Lane of Broom Hall in 1599 and the Broom Hall lands and property that belonged to John Giffard were leased to them in 1611.

John Careless, the brother of Colonel William Careless, was tenant of Broom Hall. It seems that John was the brother who stayed at home and tended the farm while his brother William was away soldiering in the Civil Wars.

It is probable that he died in 1645 leaving a son also called John who in 1656 was paying rent to the Giffard family. His mother had several children by the Colonel's brother John Careless and she married again to Edward Dearn. This Edward Dearn was tenant in

1653 and 1656 and from 1662 to 1670 John Careless shared the tenancy with him.

After Edward Dearn's death John Careless the younger became sole tenant. He had six sons; Edward was the eldest (the narrator in the story above) born most likely about 1664, then William, John, Thomas born 1669, Richard and Francis. There were also some daughters. William died in Holland and had no issue; John died in England and left no issue; Francis went to Jamaica in the West Indies in 1696/7 and sent for Richard who joined him, but both died out there without leaving any sons or daughters either.

Colonel William Careless had no surviving sons and so he left most of his estate to his adopted son Edward Careless, the grandson of his brother John. Edward was an apothecary at Worcester but also had tenancy of Broom Hall after his father's death. He and the family used the name Carlos, as granted from Charles II.

Edward was said to have married into wealth when he married Dorothy Smith of Queniborough. They had several children, Charles, William, Lawrence, Edward, John, Augustine, Elizabeth, Katherine, Dorothy and Ann. It seems that Edward and his family lived at Broom Hall at some times and other times at the Colonel's house at Green Street, Hallow near Worcester. There are records of Edward Carlos paying Hearth Tax in 1689, 1690 and 1691.

A statement in a Court case later gives an unflattering account of Edward's treatment of his father:

> "John Careless being in low condition and Edward his son, having married a woman with a good portion, he became tenant to Mr. Giffard and that soon after John Careless became very poor and went about from house to house and by licence from John----Giffard Esq built a small cottage upon the waste ground and died there in a mean condition and had not (so they believe or overheard) any maintenance or

allowance from his son, who instead of relieving him, laid him in the County Gaol."

There was a survey of the estate Broom Hall in 1704 stating that there were 132 acres and a hall. The next year Edward Carlosse of Broom Hall, apothecary, his wife and children were recorded on a list of Papists in Staffordshire.

In 1714 Edward Carlos (apothecary of Worcester) died and in his will bequeathed his estate in the district of Brewood to his wife Dorothy Carlos (formerly Smith). There is an inventory of his house and goods which includes;

> "Within the house space a litell tabell 3 ould chairs four ould stools a warming pan a drooping pan gratefier shovels and tongs...
>
> Row ould boenches a Litell Brasspot an ould ironpot and a litell Chest 4 Litell pewter dissess.
>
> Things in the over rom 2 ould beds 2 pare of Bedsteads 2 Chears and Blankits 3 pare of ould sheets."

Edward's son Charles married Mary Wilcocks and had several children, some of whose baptisms are recorded in the Catholic registers of Chillington. (Baptisms were often held in the Giffards' private chapel at Chillington Hall). Sometimes babies were baptised in the house of the parents. In 1721 Charles and Mary Careless had a son William baptised. The godparents were Richard Lloyd of Kiddemore Green and Catherine Child, sister of Charles.

Unfortunately, Charles did not manage the estate well. The account in Court for his eviction reads:

> "The Defendant by intemperant idleness and ill management being reduced to the last degree of poverty and beggary; and

being unable to manage the estate but setting out the same in parcels to neighbours to sow flax or grain and not manuring the same hath impoverished the Estate; and having suffered the house and buildings to become ruinous, the lessor, (Mr. Peter Giffard) about August last gave the Defendant warning to leave the estate at the next Lady Day and arranged for another tenant to move in."

The Statement represents Mr. Giffard as trying to help the family but he did not trust Carlos to use any gift of money wisely:

"Charles Carlos had by idleness and ill management been reduced to poverty and beggary, was unable to manage the estate and had quarrelled with neighbours. The house had become ruinous. Giffard gave warning that he was to leave the Estate next Lady Day. Some of the neighbours said to Mr. Giffard that Carlos by his drunkenness and evil ways had reduced his wife and several small children and they would become chargeable to the parish so soon as they left Broom Hall. Mr. Giffard of his own free will said he would do something for them and intended to put some money into the neighbours' hands to be employed for the benefit of the Deft (Defendant) and his family. But to be so ordered that the Deft, Carlos should not have any power to spend the same; the Deft (hearing that Mr. Giffard had so expressed himself) then and never before that time said that he had a Title to the house and all or some of his lands and would not quit possession unless Giffard would pay him down £200 and then refused to suffer Mr. Giffard's new tenant to come upon the ground."

Mr Giffard warned Charles Carlos in August of 1723 that he was to leave Broom Hall the next Lady Day, March 25th. It seems he refused to move because on April 23rd 1724 Richard Dearn (most likely a relative) sent a letter to Charles warning him Giffard was going to take action. Mrs Carlos said her husband was not at home but she expected him that night and would give the letter to him. It can be imagined the distress that Mary Carlos was suffering during these years.

The case was brought to Court. Mr. Peter Giffard wanted to put in a new tenant, Adrian Goodluck. Charles was not good at managing the estate and had already been evicted from John Lane's share of Broom Hall and replaced with Thomas Dearn, for not paying rent and letting the farm fall into disrepair and neglect. Careless lost and Goodluck gained Broom Hall. The suitability of the surnames in this event is remarkable.

Whether it was illness or drunkenness, Charles seems to have gone into a further decline. In January 1725 he wrote a will, stating that he had inherited property and plantation works from his father's brother Richard Carlos in Jamaica. It seems he was leaving this to his wife Mary Carlos and to Peter Giffard, hoping this would pay off the debts and mortgages. He died and was buried in St. Mary's churchyard Brewood the following March. Mary must have been pregnant at the time because on October 9th 1725 in the house of the late Mr. Charles Careless in Brewood his daughter Anne was baptised, the same day she was born. Her godparents were Francis Bates butcher and Mary Robinson, aunt to the child and chambermaid to Mrs. Giffard. Unfortunately, the baby Anne died 29th March the following year.

The money mentioned in his will did not seem to have the effect of restoring Broom Hall estate to the Careless family. Charles' widow Mary and her several children had to rely on the charity of the Parish or relatives. Her son, another Edward Carlos, was seven at the time of his father's death and when he grew up he became a baker at Wolverhampton. He brought a case against Peter Giffard and

Thomas Lane to the Lord High Chancellor Lord Hardwicke, appealing to have redress for his father's eviction from the estate. In this document of 1739, he details his family's descent from Colonel William Careless:

> "…descended from Colonel Carlos (who was an assistant to the late King Charles the second when he was happily preserved in the Oak) to John Carlos his brother heir at law and from the said John Carlos to John Carlos his son and heir at law and from the said last named John Carlos to Edward Carlos his eldest son and heir at law …."

Edward made his case that the Careless family owned Broom Hall and had taken a mortgage with Mr. Giffard which Charles meant to repay but failed to:

> "…your client (i.e. Edward Carloss) further showeth unto yr Lordship your clients father or some or one of his ancestors having occasion for a small sum of money applied to Peter Giffard of Chillington and Thomas Lane of Bentley to borrow the same and they or some or one of them having agreed to advance the sum of £400 yr client or his father or one of his ancestors agreed a mortgage yr client's father being a very indolent man and very careless in his affairs occasioned by a long and tedious illness and indisposition for some years before his death neglected to pay the premium of the said mortgage to Peter Giffard."

Edward went on to plead that Giffard and Lane had taken advantage of the fact that as he was only a child he had not been able to pay off the mortgage, and they had profited unfairly from the Broom Hall estate:

"Peter Giffard in or about the month of October following obtained the possession of the said premises and together with the said Lane hath ever since continued in the Receipt of the rents and profits thereof and your client (Edward Carloss) further showeth unto your Lord yr client's said father soon after in the month of May in the year of our Lord 1724 died intestate leaving yr client his eldest son and heir at law then an infant of about the age of 7 years ... his father being stripped of the possession of the said premises ... died in very indifferent circumstances and yr client his infancy being destitute of friends and not having money to pay off the said mortgage if anything was due thereon or the said Giffard and Lane ... have continued hitherto to receive the rents and profits of the premises and still insist on keeping the possession of the premises."

This plea to the Lord High Chancellor does not seem to have been successful. There is no evidence of the Careless family moving back to Broom Hall. The tragedy of Charles Careless resulted in the family losing the farm that had been their home for many generations.

Documents about Broom Hall and the Careless family

These are located at Stafford Record Office in the Giffard Papers. It is from these fascinating documents relating to the Estate of the Giffard family at Chillington Hall that most of the history of the Careless family of Broom Hall has been compiled.

Wills were studied at Lichfield Record Office but they are now relocated to Stafford Record Office.

D590/49 Lease to Thomas Careless in the reign of Henry VIII.

D590/458 Broomhall and Horsebrook lease from John Lane to John Careless, his wife Ellen and son Edward in 1599.

D590/459 1611 Messuage Broomhall let for three lives, Edward son of John and Ellen Careless, signed by Walter Giffard, 1611, during the reign of James I.

D590/59 Staffs Estates of Peter Giffard, 1654.

D590/361 Estate Maps of Chillington description of Broom Hall estate 1704.

1705 Survey of papists [Staffs Cath. History journal 13 1973].

D590/47 1715 Brewood and Broomhall, exchange of lands at Broom Hall in order to simplify the estate because Lane and Giffard properties had become so intertwined.

D590/337/7 1716 Document about Situation of Staffordshire Catholic families.

D590/794 and 393, 1719 Estate survey and tenants' names.

D590/3212/1/4 Rents and names of the Chillington Estate.

D590/32 1722 Brewood appurtenances in Broomhall.

D590/339/1-19 1724 Staffs Assizes Giffard and Goodluck vs. Carlos, Peter Giffard was the plaintiff, Charles Carlos the defendant.

The premises in question are a messuage with buildings, garden, orchard, parcels of land, meadows and pasture at Bromhall in Horsebrook near Brewood. For a great many generations, the premises have been the estate and inheritance of the Giffards of Chillington, a very ancient and worthy family. The Defendant and some of his family have long been in possession of the Estate as Tenants at Will under a yearly rent of Ten Pounds or thereabouts. (Refers to lease of 1612 to John Carloss).

D590/342 1725 1739 c1773. Concerns Carloss family. States that Laurence Carloss, only surviving son of Edward Carloss, (by this date) is heir to Richard Carloss who died in Jamaica. Careless v. Giffard and Lane re. Broomhall.

D590/696 1730 Conveyance of estate of Charles Carlos deceased in Jamaica.

D932/3/4 1736 John Careless surveyor of Brewood, mentions Thomas Carless and George Jones.

D590/339/17 1739 Edward Carlos appeal to Chancellor in which he relates his descent from Colonel Careless' brother.

D590/28 1823 John Green at Broomhall.

D590/369 Early 18th century Marston Fields.

Staffs. Estate Maps WSL.

Wills

Will of Colonel Careless, 1688 in the Prerogative Court of Canterbury, proved 19th October 1689.

Will of Edward Carlos, died 1714, located at Lichfield Record Office, now moved to Stafford.

References and Sources

M. Atkin, The Battle of Worcester 1651, (Stratford upon Avon: Harlot Publications, 2001) ISBN 0-9538117-2-7.

J. Auden, Frost (Ed.) Auden's History of Tong – Vol. 2. (Bury St. Edmunds: Arima Press 2004) ISBN 1-84549-010-X[3].

D.A. Bellenger, English and Welsh Priests 1558-1800 (Bath; Downside Abbey, 1984).

M. Bennett, Roman Catholic Royalist Officers in the North Midlands, 1642-1646. Journal of Military and Strategic Studies, Vol. 6, Issue 2 (2003).

W. Beresford, Rev. (Ed.) Memorials of Old Staffordshire, (London; George Allen and Unwin, 1909).

A.M. Broadley, The Royal Miracle, (London; Stanley Paul and Co., 1912).

J. Burke, A Genealogical and Heraldic History of the Commoners of Great Britain and Ireland, Vol. I, (London: Colburn, 1834).

N. Carlisle, An inquiry into the place and quality of the Gentlemen of His Majesty's ... privy chamber ..., Royal Households by Nicholas Carlisle (London: Payne and Foss, 1829).

D. Casserly, Massacre: The Storming of Bolton, (Stroud, Gloucestershire: Amberly Publishers, 2010) ISBN 978-1-84868-976-3.

Catholic Records Society journals.

A. Fea, The Flight of the King, (London: Methuen 1897, second ed. 1908).

H. Foley, Records of the English province of the Society of Jesus Vol. I, (London: Burns and Oates, 1877).

A. Fraser, King Charles II, (London: Weidenfeld and Nicolson, 1979).

A. Fraser, editor, The Lives of the Kings and Queens of England (London: published by Book Club Associates, by arrangement with Weidenfeld and Nicolson, 1975).

Count Grammont, Memoirs of the Court of Charles the Second and the Boscobel Narratives, edited by Sir Walter Scott, (York Street London: Bohn, 1846).

H. Grazebrook, The Heraldry of Worcestershire. (London: John Russell Smith, 1873) pp.102-103.

M. Greenslade, Catholic Staffordshire, (Leominster: Gracewing, 2006) ISBN 0-85244-655-1.

F.W. Hamilton, Sir, The Origin and History of the First or Grenadier Guards. (London: John Murray, 1874).

Holt, English Jesuits 1650-1829, located in Birmingham Diocesan Archives at St Chad's Cathedral Birmingham.

D. Horowitz, A History of Brewood (Brewood, 1992 edn) ISBN 1-85421-011-4.

J. Hughes (Ed.) The Boscobel Tracts, (Edinburgh and London: William Blackwood, 1857).

R. Jeffery, Discovering Tong, (Tong, Shropshire: Tong Parochial Church Council, 2007).

W. Matthews Charles II's Escape from Worcester, (Berkeley and Los Angeles, University of California Press, 1966).

R. Ollard, The Escape of Charles II after the Battle of Worcester, (London: Robinson 2002: Hodder and Stoughton Ltd, 1966).

M.B. Rowland's, Those Who Have Gone Before Us, (Birmingham: published by the Archdiocese of Birmingham Historical Commission, 1989).

C.J. Lyon, Personal History of King Charles II. (Edinburgh: Stevenson, 1851).

J.H. Smith, (1874) Brewood: a résumé historical and topographical, (London: W. Parke, 1874).

P. Warner, (S.J.) History of England, Persecution of Catholics and the Presbyterian Plot, Part 2. Warner was a Jesuit priest who was chaplain to James II. His book can be found in the Catholic Record Society journal, Vol. 48 (1955) edited by Prof. T.A. Birrell.

R.A. Lewis, advisory Officer for History, His Majesty's Miraculous Preservation Staffordshire County Council Education Department /Local History Source Book G.14, (1973). This booklet has extracts from;

Blount's Boscobel, written by a Catholic lawyer Thomas Blount in 1660.

An Exact Narrative and Relation of His Most Sacred Majesty's Escape from Worcester (1660) Original Account.

Whitgreaves' Account of Charles II's Preservation.

The King's Account as told to Pepys.

T. Spicer, The Battle of Worcester, 1651 (2009) ISBN 978-0952-148-852.

Victoria County History of Staffordshire, abbreviated to V.C.H. Staffs.

William Salt Library next to the Stafford Record Office in Eastgate Street, Stafford. On the shelves there is a series of volumes called the Collections for a History of Staffordshire (Staffordshire Record Society, formerly William Salt Archaeological Society) abbreviated to S.H.C.

Original Sources

Chillington baptism and marriage registers located at Birmingham Archdiocesan Archives (BAA) at St Chad's Cathedral Birmingham. Brewood parish registers for St Mary's C. of E. parish church located at Lichfield Record Office.

Giffard Papers, a collection of documents concerning the Giffard family and their estate at Chillington, located at Stafford Record Office.

Further Reading – Historical Novels

William Careless appears as a character in the novel 'Boscobel or the Royal Oak: A Tale of the Year 1651,' by William Harrison Ainsworth, first published in 1871. As William Carlis, he is also found in 'Royal Escape' (1938) a historical novel written by Georgette Heyer.

Notes on Sources for Each Chapter

Prologue

Who was Ellen? Ellen who features in the Prologue was the step daughter of Walter Evans who bought Boscobel in 1812. He made some alterations, trying to present the building in keeping with its romantic history and to restore it to how he thought it would have looked at the time when King Charles stayed there. Ellen had two older sisters, Elizabeth and Frances, and they and their mother took part enthusiastically in furnishing the house and designing the garden according to how it was described in old accounts. They restored the arbour on the mound where Charles had spent the Sunday afternoon reading. The pebble inscription in the garden, which mentions King Charles, was laid by Ellen when she was not much more than twenty and she very much enjoyed the work.

Reference
Guide book to Boscobel House published by English Heritage, 'The Romantic Idea of Boscobel' by J.J. West (1987).

Chapter 1: Testimony of John Careless, tenant of Broom Hall

Victoria County History Vol. V History of Brewood Michael W. Greenslade and Margaret Midgley. Most of the information in there is from the Collection of Giffard Papers at Chillington located at Staffordshire Record Office.

Some information about the pedigree of the Careless family is from Alan Fea, (1897, second ed. 1908) The Flight of the King, London.

John Careless (Johannes Careless) husbandman at Tong in the county of Salop was named as recusant in 1600 in the Significations of Excommunications in the Diocese of Coventry and Lichfield EL2163, located in the Catholic Record Society journal, Vol. 60, page 114, Recusant Documents from Ellesmere MS. Edited by Petti. As Tong is only three miles from Broom Hall I have assumed it was the same John Careless but that may not be the case.

The quote about Peter Giffard's recusancy is in SHC new series V p.175 and Cal. S.P. Dom 1639-1640 p.554.

The quote describing Wolverhampton is from R. Lee "The Spirituall Spring". A sermon preached at St. Paul's (1625) a copy of which is at the William Salt Library Stafford.

William Careless is said to have married the sister of Sampson Fox, (source unknown). A survey of papists records William and Dorothy Careless at Brewood. [Staffs Catholic History v (1965) A list of Staffordshire Recusants by A.J. Kettle].

The date for Colonel William Careless's first son William being born is based on the account in Foley, Henry (1877) Records of the English province of the Society of Jesus Vol. I, Burns and Oates, London, where the son writes that he was thirteen years old when his father was governor of Tong Castle from April 1644.

The source for William Careless joining Thomas Leveson's regiment is M. Bennett, (2003) Roman Catholic Royalist Officers in the North Midlands, 1642-1646. Journal of Military and Strategic Studies, Vol. 6, Issue 2.

Chapter 2: Testimony of Colonel Thomas Leveson, a Royal Commander

www.blackcountrybugle.co.uk/leveson-dudleys-past/story-20148796.../story.html

wiki.bcw-project.org/royalist/foot-regiments/thomas-leveson

wiki.bcw-project.org/royalist/dragoon-regiments/thomas-leveson

Catholic Staffordshire by Michael Greenslade pages 97, 99, 103, 105.

S.H.C. new series vi, p.315; order for Stafford Castle to be demolished S.H.C. 4th series I, p.21.

Shaw Staffs. i, general history, pages 55, 60-62: ii pages 144-6.

Some Letters of the Civil War, S.H.C. 1941, pages 142-143, and 146-147.

R.E. Sherwood, Civil Strife in the Midlands 1642-1651 (Chichester 1974) pages 67, 212.

Johnson and Vaisey, (eds), Staffordshire and the Great Rebellion p.68.

The capture of Chillington S.H.C. 1941 pages 138-9.

Chillington regarrisoned, Shaw Staffs. ii page 145.

Auden, John, E. (2004) Joyce Frost (Ed.) Auden's History of Tong – Volume 2. Bury St. Edmunds. ISBN 1-84549-010-X Page 30.

D. Casserly, Massacre: The Storming of Bolton, (Stroud, Gloucestershire Amberly Publishers 2010). ISBN 978-1-84868-976-3 Page 126-129 and page 188.

Chapter 3: Testimony of Dorothy Careless, wife of Colonel William Carlos

Findmypast website at Stafford and Lichfield Record offices; the parish registers of St. Leonard's Marston, near Stafford.

www.findmypast.co.uk/...all.../the-staffordshire-and-diocese-of-lichfield-collections;

Dorothy Fox is on the baptismal register 1609 at Marston near Stafford, daughter of Walter Fox of Salt.

In the prerogative court of Canterbury there is a will for 1651 for Walter Fox gent, of Salt, (a village near Stafford), proved 19th July by his grandson William Carles of Brewood. [That was William Carless who became a priest]. Probate under supervision of William Smith gent. of Chillington, parish of Brewood. In it Walter Fox names Elizabeth Hawkins and Dorothy Carlos as his daughters and heirs, his sons William, Richard and Sampson, his daughters Katherine Ensor, Mary Fox and Margaret Fox, grandson William Carlos, Walter Fox and William Fox, sons of Richard and William B(?)ralow. [The children of Margaret Fox and Mary Fox are mentioned, so they may be daughters-in-law]

There is a burial record for Dorothy Careless at Hallow near Worcester, where William Careless owned a house;

Burial register St Philip and St James at Hallow 26th June 1676 for Dorothy Careless.

The information about the Pierrepoint family at Tong Castle is from Discovering Tong by Robert Jeffery, page 30.

A very useful source is the Guide book to the High House at Stafford, "The Ancient High House", research and text by Fiona Sheridan, published by Addax Media Ltd. for the time when Colonel Careless was held prisoner there.

Chapter 4: Testimony of Charles Giffard, a member of the Royalist Army

M. Greenslade, Catholic Staffordshire pages 44-45 about John Giffard.

A. Fraser, biography of King Charles II, for the account of the Battle of Worcester, pages 133-146.

Staffordshire County Council "His Majesty's Miraculous Preservation" pages 4-7.

M. Atkin, The Battle of Worcester 1651 (Battleground Britain) ISBN: 978-1-84415-080-9.

The Battle of Worcester 1651, a collection of essays, published by the Battle of Worcester Society, 2012, ISBN: 978-0-9572421-1-1.

T. Spicer, The Battle of Worcester, 1651, Mark Stacey, ISBN: 978-0-95214-885-2.

W. Matthews Charles II's Escape from Worcester, (Berkeley and Los Angeles, University of California Press, 1966).

D. Craine, (1995) Manannan's Isle, The Manx Museum and National Trust, ISBN 978-0-901106-10-0.

Draper, Peter (1864), "Defeat of Charles and Capture of James, Earl of Derby", The house of Stanley; including the soeges of Lathom House with notices of relative and co-temporary incidents, T. Hutton.

Websites

http://www.historyofparliamentonline.org/volume/1509-1558/member/giffard-john-1534-1613

bcw-project.org/military/third-civil-war/Worcester

www.battlefieldstrust.com > ... > The Civil Wars > The Worcester Campaign 1651

https://en.wikipedia.org/wiki/Battle_of_Worcester

Battle of Wigan Lane Wikipedia

http://www.thebattleofworcestersociety.org.uk/

Chapter 5: Testimony of Richard Penderel of Hobbal Grange

Richard Penderel was called "Trusty Dick" by the King, who must have been very grateful for his company for those two difficult days and nights of frantic flight. This narrative was drawn from the five contemporary accounts: Boscobel by Blount, Fr. Huddleston's Account, Whit greave's Account, The King's Account and the "Exact Narrative and Relation of His Most Sacred Majesty's Escape from Worcester". Richard died in 1672.

Chapter 6: Testimony of His Majesty King Charles II, by the Grace of God Sovereign of England, Scotland, Wales and Ireland

This is also based on the five contemporary accounts mentioned above. The King loved to talk about his escape and his adventures and dictated an account to Samuel Pepys. Sometimes he did not recall details accurately.

Chapter 7: Testimony of William Careless (the younger), son of Colonel William Careless

Brother Henry Foley Records of the English Province Society of Jesus Vol. V (1881). This gives a brief life of Fr. William Carlos, alias Dorrington and relates the letter he wrote when applying to train at the English college in Rome.

Note: Dorrington was the name of a priest who came from Mucklestone, a village in Staffordshire near Market Drayton, about 30 miles from Brewood. William Carlos may have chosen his alias from him or the Dorrington family who built the High House in Staffordshire.

Fr. Michael Archer, Catholic Truth Society booklet on John Southworth (2010) ISBN 978-1-86082-668-9.

Bellenger, English and Welsh Priests 1558-1800.

Holt, English Jesuits 1650-1829.

Booklet on Kelvedon Hatch.

Catholic Record Society 40/54 and 55/548.

Essex Recusants journals; 5/35 and 95, 9/108 located at St. Chad's Birmingham Archdiocesan Archives.

Edward S. Worrall Eighteenth Century Jesuit Priests in Essex, Essex Recusants Vol 5 (1959) and Vol 9.

Necrology English Provinces SJ (1561-1937) pages 113-4, 43ff9-12

The death of Thomas Careless in 1665 was found from Ancestry and Findmypast websites as well as being referred to by Alan Fea, Flight of the King.

The tombstone of Thomas Carlos in All Saints church at Fulham has an inscription which reads;

Here lyeth interred the body of
THOMAS CARLOS sonn of Co-
Leinell WILLIAM CARLOS of
Staffordshire who departed
This life in the 25th yeare of
His age on the 19 day of May 1665
Tis not bare name that noble fathers give
To worthy sonnes though dead in them they live
For in his progeny tis heaven's decree
Man only can on earth immortal bee
But heaven gives soules with grace doth sometimes bend
Early to God their nice and Soveraigne end
Thus whilst that earth concern'd did hope to see
The noble father living still in thee
Care lesse of earth to heaven thou didst aspire
And wee on earth CARLOS in thee desire.

From Royal Households by Nicholas Carlisle publishers Payne and Frost 1829, pages 176 and 177, Gentlemen of the Privy Chamber: "Colonel William Carlis, or Careless, of Bromhall, in the county of Stafford, – of good Parentage and approved valour, – who contrived the concealment of King Charles the Second in The Royal Oak in the Forest of Boscobel, after the disastrous Battle of Worcester. For his particular service and fidelity both to Charles the First and Second, the last of those Sovereigns, by Letters patent, gave him the Name of "Carlos," (being in Spanish, "Charles"), with a new and appropriate Coat of Arms."

Sources for Titus Oates Plot, A. Fraser, *King Charles II* and M. Greenslade, *Catholic Staffordshire*.

Websites

www.jesuit.org.uk/archives-jesuits-britain

www.historyhouse.co.uk/houses/The History of Kelvedon Hatch

www.cts-online.org.uk

[Father William Carlos, professed Jesuit priest, died January 10th, 1679, four days after his vows of final profession. He had been on Titus Oates list of wanted recusants, but his illness took him to his Maker before any action was taken to arrest him.]

Chapter 8: Testimony of Edward Carlos, Apothecary of Worcester, adopted son of Colonel William Carlos

Alan Fea "Flight After Worcester" for the pedigree of the Careless family. Note. This family tree in Fea's book gives Edward Carlos as the son of John Careless, Colonel Careless' brother but it seems more likely that Edward was the grandson of that John Careless, as his birth date, 1664 seems quite late.

Staffordshire Record Society 4th series vol. 11 at William Salt Library, "A Survey of Papists, 1657".

The account of King Charles banning public bonfires is from P. Warner's History of England Persecution of Catholics and the Presbyterian Plot, paragraph 458.

D. Fowkes and M.W. Greenslade, "A List of Staffordshire Recusants 1678-80", Staffordshire Catholic History xxiv (1990), pp1sqq.

A. Fraser, Kings and Queens of England for account of reign of James II page 243, (1975).

M. Greenslade, Catholic Staffordshire pages 148-151, 153-154, 159-160 for the situation for Catholics in Staffordshire during the reign of James II and the revolution of William of Orange.

M. Greenslade, Bishop Leyburn at Stafford and Wolverhampton Staffordshire Catholic History ii pages 19-26.

J.A. Hilton and others (Eds), Bishop Leyburn's Confirmation Register of 1687 (Wigan, 1997) pages 234-40, 306.

BBC programme by Lucy Worsley, British History's Biggest Fibs series 1 The Glorious Revolution, 23rd January 2017.

Will of Colonel William Careless, recorded in A. Fea's Flight after Worcester and also available online through Ancestry.

Records located at Worcester Record Office of the Hearth Tax at Green Street at Hallow, 1689, 1690 and 1691 paid by Edward Carlos.

Website

www.catholicsaints.info/blessed-john-gavan

List of Illustrations

Front cover: portrait of Colonel Careless, a miniature in a locket at the Victoria and Albert Museum.

Page 28: The Ancient High House in Stafford where William Careless was imprisoned in 1645. Reproduced under licence with thanks to the Staffordshire Archives and Heritage. Ref: SCBPC-2009-296 (129/24278). Source: Staffordshire County Buildings Picture Collection.

Page 38: A map showing the march of the Royalist and Parliamentary troops from Scotland to the Battle of Worcester. It is based on the map from Worcester Archaeological Service in Malcolm Atkin's book, The Battle of Worcester 1651, published by Harlot Publications 2001. Malcolm Atkin kindly gave permission to use it.

Page 46: Inn at Ombersley, photo from the website of KINGS ARMS, Main Road, Ombersley, Droitwich, Worcestershire, WR9 0EW.

Page 48: A map of Charles' escape route from Worcester compiled from the places that he rode through. References are from a National Trust booklet Charles II Escape Route Worcester to Shoreham published by Craven Design and Print; Richard Ollard's The Escape of Charles II after the battle of Worcester, (London, Robinson 1966); a booklet, *His Majesty's Miraculous Preservation* from Staffordshire County Council Education Department Local History Source Book G.14 by R.A. Lewis, and also from Google Maps which gives the approximate timing of the journey.

Page 52: Painting of White Ladies and Boscobel. South view of the house and garden within a stockade set in a wood. Various items of interest are numbered and described. From the Doncaster edition of *The history of the rebellion and civil wars in England begun in the year 1641*, (originally written by Earl Edward Hyde Clarendon in 1717), 1809. Artist: 'Boocock Don [?]' [Signature very faint.] Reproduced under licence from the Staffordshire Archives and Heritage. Ref: SCBPC-2009-275. Source Staffordshire County Buildings Picture Collection. White Ladies Priory is now a barely-surviving ruin and Boscobel House a much-restored and extended seventeenth-century farmhouse; they are about a mile apart on the Shropshire-Staffordshire border near Bishop's Wood. White Ladies appears to the left; Boscobel to the right and the Royal Oak in the centre foreground.

Page 55: A sketch map (not to scale) of the area around Brewood and Boscobel in Staffordshire, showing the houses featuring in the story of Charles II's escape.

Page 64: Portrait of Richard Penderel by kind permission of The National Trust. This portrait of Richard Penderel, looking honest, trustworthy and reliable, is after Gerard Soest by Richard Houston (Dublin 1721/22, London 1775) CMS-MOS00384 by permission of National Trust Images/Claire Reeves.

Page 66: King Charles II in Boscobel Wood by Isaac Fuller (1606-1672). The second of a set of five scenes that commemorate Charles

II's dramatic escape from Parliamentarian forces following his defeat in the final battle of the civil wars. Episodes such as the king taking refuge in the 'Royal Oak' passed into popular culture through written accounts, plays and prints. This scene depicts an event on 6 September when Charles II was escorted by the Penderels to nearby Boscobel Wood, where he met Colonel William Careless. Careless had fought at the Battle of Worcester and was also a fugitive from Parliamentarian forces. It is notable that Charles II is not shown as the 21-year-old he was in 1651 but as the mature king following the Restoration. This image is under licence from the National Portrait Gallery. Primary Collection NPG 5248. The five paintings can be viewed on the NPG website but unfortunately, they are not on public display at the Gallery but in storage at Southwark, where they can only be viewed by appointment.

Page 68: "King Charles and Colonel Careless in the oak." showing King Charles II climbing into the tree. Published by J. Hatchard, Piccadilly, June 1806. Ref: SV-II.113b (45/7437) reproduced under licence from the William Salt Library, Eastgate Street Stafford.

Page 76: The parlour at Moseley Old Hall where King Charles went to hide after his visit to Boscobel. On the wall is a portrait of Thomas Whitgreave who helped the King. He later wrote an account of the time the King was sheltered there. Moseley Old Hall is a National Trust property and this photograph is by kind permission of the National Trust.

Page 83: Painting of Saint John Southworth which is at Westminster Cathedral. This photograph was taken by the husband of Anne Marie Micallef, Finance Officer and Co-ordinator of the Guild of Saint John Southworth, who kindly sent it to me.

Page 87: The coat of arms granted to Colonel Careless, renamed Carlos. This can be found in T. Blount's *Boscobel* (1822) edition facing page 86. Reproduced by permission of William Salt Library, Stafford. The motto is "Subditus Fidelis Regis et Regni Salus" which means "A servant faithful to the King and the safety of the Kingdom". The description of the coat of arms is, "He bears upon an Oake proper in a gold field a Fesse gules, charged with three Regal Crowns of the second: by the name of Carlos. And for his Crest a Civic Crown or oaken Garland with a Sword and Scepter crossed through it Saltierwise."

Page 102: Portrait of Saint John Gavan martyred in 1679 during the Titus Oates persecution and mentioned by Father William Carlos. It can be found in H. Foley *Records of the English Province of the Society of Jesus*, facing page 454. Thanks to the Birmingham Archdiocesan Archives.

Page 109: Portrait of Father John Huddleston (1608-1698) at Moseley Old Hall Staffordshire by kind permission of the National Trust.

Page 120: This oval locket made of copper gilt is in the Victoria and Albert Museum, Room 54 case 14, in the metalwork collection. It dates from the second half of the 17th century but the maker is unknown. On the front is an engraved family crest and the Latin inscription, "Subditus Fidelis Regis & Regni salus" which means "A subject faithful to his King is the safety of the Kingdom." This image is reproduced with permission from the Victoria and Albert Museum.

Page 158: Three photos of St. Mary and St. Chad, parish church at Brewood, are by kind permission of Rev. Philip Moon. This beautiful historic church is well worth a visit.

Family tree of the Careless/ Carlos family at Broom Hall Staffordshire

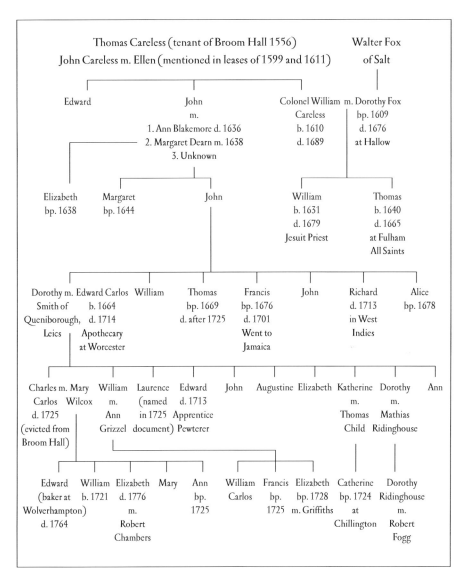

Note: The family tree in Alan Fea's book, *Flight of the King,* gives Edward Carlos as the son of John Careless, Colonel Careless' brother but it seems more likely that Edward was the grandson of that John Careless for the following reasons:

John Careless married in 1638 but Edward, who was the eldest child, was born in 1664. It is more likely that he is another generation down. [Brewood parish registers]

A document in the Giffard collection records that Colonel Careless had a brother John, who had a son John, who had a son Edward. (D590/339/17 Edward Carlos' appeal to Chancellor in which he relates his descent from Colonel Careless' brother. Dated 1739).

The account of the appeal of Goodluck versus Careless also relates that John Careless had a son John Careless whose son was Edward.

The plaque in memory of William Careless in St. Mary the Virgin and St. Chad, parish church of Brewood.

Tomb of John Giffard and his wife Joyce Leveson in the parish church of St. Mary and St. Chad at Brewood.

Gravestone for Colonel William Careless in the graveyard of the parish church at Brewood.

Index